DAYS OF OUR LIVES...

CREATIVE WRITING FROM YORKSHIRE

Edited by Heather Killingray

First published in Great Britain in 2001 by
YOUNG WRITERS
Remus House,
Coltsfoot Drive,
Peterborough, PE2 9JX
Telephone (01733) 890066

HB ISBN 0 75432 710 8
SB ISBN 0 75432 711 6

FOREWORD

This year Young Writers proudly presents a showcase of the best 'Days Of Our Lives . . .' short stories, from up-and-coming writers nationwide.

To write a short story is a difficult exercise. We made it more challenging by setting the theme of 'A Day In The Life Of Someone From The Second Millennium', using no more than 250 words! Much imagination and skill is required. *Days Of Our Lives . . . Creative Writing From Yorkshire* achieves and exceeds these requirements. This exciting anthology will not disappoint the reader.

The thought, effort, imagination and hard work put into each story impressed us all, and again, the task of editing proved demanding due to the quality of entries received, but was nevertheless enjoyable.

We hope you are as pleased as we are with the final selection and that you continue to enjoy *Days Of Our Lives . . . Creative Writing From Yorkshire* for many years to come.

CONTENTS

Nigel Bancroft	70
Cassie Williams	71
Bethany Cammiss	72
Rachel Morley	73
Melissa Lacey	74
Catriona Ferguson	75
Rebecca Moses	76
Adam Rollinson	77
Jacob Lilley	78
Rachael Colclough	79
Chloe Marsden	80
Stephanie Muscroft	81
Sarah George	82
Amy Ryder	83
Emma Coates	84
Matthew Featherstone	85
Jenna Partington	86
Aaron Dixon	87
Anthony Parker	88
Luke Robinson	89
Brogan Bell	90
Ryan Whitehead	91
Kathryn Richardson	92
Jasmine Khouja	93
Eleanor Noble	94
Florentina Plummer	95
Martin Durrant	96
Cari Jones	97
Vicky Burgess	98
Timothy Godfrey	99
Edward Noble	100
Chris Kew	101
Lauren Spence	102
Victoria Bishop	103
Lauren Fox	104
Aimee Hirst	105

Crowlees CE(C) J&I School

Matthew Stevenson	106
Daniel Conway	107
Jordan Senior	108
Joanna Barker	110
Sanniya Khan	111
Megan Aguirregoicoa	112
Taheri Behnam	113
Emma Lockwood	114
Jake Crossley	115
Graham Kirkby	116
Jenny Chester	117
Danny Broadley	118
Daniel Jones	119
Stephanie Clayton	120
Kate Ramsden	122
Kimberley Delaney	124
Laura Brocklebank	125
Ben Brownhill	126
Thomas Stratford	127
James Rotchell	128
Brooke Oliver	129
Lois Rowling	130
Rachel Wise	131
Sam Taylor	132
Jessica Blackburn	133
Anthony Senior	134
William Best	135
Lucy McDermott	136
Stephanie Harrison	137
Stefani Fox	138
Thomas Moggridge	139
Matthew Chandler	140
Daniel Wright	141
Ben Renshaw	142
Ross Taylor	143
Rebecca Sheard	144
Alexandra Stratford	145

Greasbrough J&I School

Heath View Community Primary School

Hempland Primary School

Leopold Primary School

Ley Top Primary School

Lindhead Primary School

Helen Sutcliffe	282
Michaela Wyatt	284
James Rushworth	285
Sophie McNeill	286
Tanith Horner	287
Emily Riley	288
Sarah Gerrard	289
Laura Houlihan	290

Spennithorne CE Primary School

Alice Miller	291
Colette Cowley	292

Throstle Farm Primary School

Kurtis Walker	293
Sarah Blackburn	294
Stephanie Morton	295
Natalie Ferguson	296
Leanna Jordan	298
Luke Prentice	299

West Heslerton CE Primary School

Joanna Mason	300
George Trowsdale	301
Genevieve Lee Edwards	302
Kristian Wilkinson	304
Patrick Young	305
James Bailey	306
Becky Mason	307
Beth Clay	308
Joe Clay	309
Lorna Gledhill	310
Eleanor Mennell	311
Thomas Milner	312
Kirsty Whitley	313
Laura Mason	314
Annabel Watson	315
Anne Lumley	316

The Stories

A DAY IN THE LIFE OF MY HAMSTER

Hi, my hamster is ginger and white. It is a boy. He is called George, he is quite fat and he always wants food. He has a big cage with a wheel and a house. It has not just got a downstairs, it has got an upstairs too. So his food goes upstairs in a bowl. He has got a door downstairs and one upstairs. This is so I can put my hand through the top and put the food there. The downstairs one is so I can get him out to play. He loves playing with anyone and he has never, ever in my whole life bitten me. I do not think he will ever bite me. He is one year old and I think they only live for two years but some live longer than that.

The outside of the cage is yellow. His drink bottle is white and red, it is not the biggest. I have to wash and dry his cage, food bowl, house and wheel and his drink bottle. Every week I do it on a Sunday. He lives in our kitchen in his cage. He sometimes goes with his ball outside and this is green. He loves doing that but sometimes the cat runs after him. But she cannot get him. In his house we put tissue paper and he puts this all over his cage.

Rebekah Amiri (10)
Alne County Primary School

A DAY IN THE LIFE OF KATHRYN

'Bother! I've overslept, I'm going to be late for the bus Mum,' I shouted.
'Well come and have your breakfast then,' Mum shouted.
'I haven't got time, bye,' I bellowed! I had to run to the bus stop, eventually I got there and I was on the bus going to school. I got to school alright and Rosie, Rachael, Sophie, Becky and Hannah were all there talking. They all said hello to me and I said Hi back! Then the whistle went, we all got into line and went into the classroom. We had Mr B. Oh No, we've got maths. I hate maths. You see I like English, though we're doing that after play so I sat down and got on with my maths. Well I did about five minutes of it because I started daydreaming. So I got told off and I had to stay in at play and do it, but then I heard everybody coming back in so I packed up. Now we're doing English. I love English but unfortunately it was nearly lunchtime. I had a pack-up with Rosie, Sophie, Hannah and Becky but Rachael has a dinner, yuck!. Dinner was over and we all went out for play but it was quite boring, but then the whistle went so we went back inside. Mr B read us a story. I quite like stories but I just drew in my rough book, but then we went out to play, we all played Bulldog, then I went home.

Rachel Armstrong (11)
Alne County Primary School

A DAY IN THE LIFE OF A LADYBIRD

'It's quite a happy life, flying around from leaf to leaf, just being a ladybird.' I was singing whilst having my breakfast. Then I saw it, my most favourite food in the world! An *aphid*! It was on the bottom leaf of the middle cabbage in the cabbage patch, which was just below me. I took a dive, straight for it and landed right on top of it. I took one bite out of it and I was hooked. It was absolutely scrumptious. I'd finished off the aphid and I was flying above the geraniums when I saw a greenfly, attacking a leaf. I thought it must be my lucky day. I took another dive and I scored a direct hit. One aphid and one greenfly, all packed into my tiny, little stomach.

I was tired, so I flew to my favourite part of the garden, which was the raspberry patch and rested on a raspberry leaf. Suddenly a finger came down onto my leaf and made it wobble, so I had no choice except to climb onto it. The finger went right across the garden into a shadowy place. I was put into a very dark, square thing and suddenly it was pitch-black. *Arrgghhh! Arrgghh! I can't breathe! Arrgghhh, I'm choking.*

Claire Boddy (10)
Alne County Primary School

A DAY IN THE LIFE OF ROCKY

A day in the life of Rocky would be, let's say, explosive, deadly and even doomed because something like this would happen. Rocky would meet his friend Tom, chat like friends do. Then they would make war and in the end one of them would have an axe in their head. So you see what I mean, now let's get into Rocky and see what it's like for Rocky.

'Hi,' Rocky would say.
'Hi,' Tom would say.
Lucozade's the best, no Cola is, Lucozade, Cola, brrr . . . goes the machine gun, stsss . . . boom goes the bomb! Boom goes the wipe out 2000 and so on. So let's go into Rocky's biggest adventure, bombs away, where Rocky and Tom meet a strange cannon which comes alive and makes big trouble. Let's go into it, one, two, three, boom, boom.
'Help,' said Tom 'if we move the rock on top of it we can kill it, one, two, three!'

Crash! 'Who-ooo,' said Tom, so the crazy cannon went boom! Bye, bye and boy it took a lot of work. So thank you for reading a day in the life of . . . Rocky, bye.

Ben Brown (10)
Alne County Primary School

A DAY IN THE LIFE OF ROSIE BURCH

Last Wednesday is the day I'll tell you about. I got up at 7.30, got dressed, ran outside and hurried to the bus stop just in time to catch the bus. I jumped on board, bought my ticket and hopped into the very best seat, the back seat. Well that kind of tells you what I'm like so I don't really need to tell you much except that my name's Rosie Burch. I'm nine and I'm friendly. Well, anyway when the bus stopped at my stop I skidded down the bus and jumped off and if you're wondering why I am in such a hurry, it's because I've just got £10 pocket money from Mum and Dad and there is this new shop called Scooter. Everyone is talking about it. So when I'd skipped round York for a bit I decided to ask someone, an old man actually, where it was. He told me the way and I plodded off. Oh yeah, I forgot to tell you, it's my birthday today and guess who forgot to get me a cake, a present and even a party. Mum had. I had it all planned out as well. Well at least nearly all planned out. Anyway, when I went into Scooter I chose a Laser I, paid for it and then walked out the shop. When I got home I opened the door and there was a great, big cake on the table. So I walked into the lounge and *surprise!*

Rosie Burch (9)
Alne County Primary School

A DAY IN THE LIFE OF MY DOG ROSS

It all started when I was thinking about a day in the life of Ross and that's when it all started.

'Hey, I'm Ross, my best friend's Chequa and she is the boss around here and Charlotte, that's my other best friend. She always plays with the ball with me and sometimes she's horrible to me but most of the time she's nice.'

'Oh my God here she comes, she's heading for the ball and she's kicked it, it's coming for me. Jumping, got it, ha, ha, I've got the ball and you haven't, go away or I'll bite.'

'Here Ross,' she always says and she kicks another ball and when I fall for it she gets the one I left and it all starts off again. 'Bye Ross I have to go for my tea.' Did someone say tea?

The next moment I was on the floor with my head bleeding. Then quickly I'm back into the feel of being a dog. Then Mum comes out with the dog bowl and says 'Tea.'

Chequa runs up so I follow. 'Sit Ross, sit Chequa.'
Then Mum says 'Charlotte.' Then I turned back into a dog.
'Chequa, are you eating all that?'
'Yes, I am, now leave me alone.'
Then a human licking a bowl with a cut head, and then a dog, finally I turned back into a human and stayed like that.

Charlotte Chambers (9)
Alne County Primary School

A Day In The Life Of A Teacher

What a racket! This class is disgraceful. If I could just get another job I would be out of here in a flash! By the way my name is James Jones, and I am really mad this morning. If this class doesn't shut up I'll get my cane out and . . . I didn't get the chance to finish my sentence. A little, fat kid bumped into me. 'Hey, watch where you're going kid.' These kids have no respect for their elders. I wish all kids were like the kids that went to the science school. At that school the kids have so much fun. They are never naughty. 'Wish I worked there,' I said to myself in a low mutter. 'Class, listen up. Today we are just going to do games and design technology.' A big shout of yay and yippee was heard. At last the class was under control. For the first time in my life I actually enjoyed a lesson.

At lunchtime I went outside to have a cigarette. Someone was shouting 'Oi you, nutter person, you shouldn't smoke, it's bad for your health.' Whoever said that was as good as dead. I was going to put a cigarette in this person's mouth and not let it out. That's when I saw it was a kid.
'Go inside kid,' I said, and for the second time that day I thought I should get a different job.

Philip Darby (10)
Alne County Primary School

A DAY IN THE LIFE OF A WOLF

My name's Sophie, I have a dad called Tony he's really wicked! One day I went camping with my dad.
'Do you want to go fishing?' Tony said.
'No, I want to go bird watching,' I said.
'Alright then,' said Tony.

I saw a cave and decided to head towards it. I suddenly fell over a stone, I screamed. Dad ran up to me but also something came out of the cave it was a wolf! We ran until we got back to the car, we looked at the time it was 10pm.

The next day I woke up as a wolf! I stepped out of the tent and I went up to the cave. As I ran there I felt my grey, glossy coat shine in the sun. I finally reached the cave, there stood in front of me was a wolf. I held up my paw, he did the same thing. We walked in the cave, I lay down. Somehow I talked to him.
He said, 'Go get some meat.'
'Yes,' I said.
We ran till we got to my tent. My dad stared at me as though he knew me . . . He jumped back, I saw on his watch it was 2pm. I ran back to the cave and went to sleep. The wolf growled and bit me on my leg. I suddenly woke up, I was a human again but it was still there!

Sophie Davies (10)
Alne County Primary School

A Day In The Life Of My Dog

I was in the car on the way back from school and I wished I was my dog Betty. She is a black Labrador. She is 3 years old. She is silky and smooth. Well, when I got back home I went out to my garden with Betty. I wished again that I was Betty because she doesn't have to go to school or do homework. Then suddenly I turned into my dog and Betty turned into me. Me, I mean Betty, threw the ball for me. I didn't go after it. I tried to tell Betty that I was her and she was me but my voice just barked. I ran into the house, I needed a glass of water. I went to the cupboard, I reached out and instead of hands I had paws. Then I thought if I was a dog I would have to drink out of a dog bowl so I went over to the dog bowl and thought Betty will have to drink from a cup. Now I know how Betty feels and I certainly wasn't looking forward to teatime. I bet Betty was though, I hope it doesn't last very long. I drank out of the dog bowl it was OK, at least I changed the water before I went outside so Betty had not drunk out of it. Teatime came around five minutes before that I turned back to my usual self.

Kimberley Downey (10)
Alne County Primary School

A Day In The life Of Super Baby

This story is about my own comic character, he's called Super Baby.

'Waa! Not fair, Mummy give sweeties, not fair.'
'No darling, it's bad for your teeth and they will drop out! Now come on let's get in the car and get to playschool.
'Bye!' As I ran out of the car, she was talking to the other mums so she probably didn't hear me. When I got into the playground I noticed that Josh who is my friend was being bullied so I walked over and there he was being hit. I couldn't stand for this so I said 'Leave him alone!' And he hit me, so I hit him back, he went somersaulting in the air and then he hit the floor hard and he was rolling around in pain.

A teacher came over and said, 'Who did this?' So I used my brainwashing powers and brainwashed her to think that he fell over so she let us go.
'You were brrrrilliant,' said Josh with a smile on his face, he likes going brrrrrr! I went in and we played games all day. At hometime my mum collected me from playschool, she walked me to the car.
'Had a good day?'
'Yes.'
When we got home my mum put on the news, it said large sweets are attacking the city, so I changed into my outfit as quick as a flash and flew to the city. There they were wrecking the city, there was a sweet cane, a packet of gums and a gobstopper. So I tugged up a lamp post, there was a bees nest so I stuck my hand in and got a handful of honey, stuck it on some branches and put it on so it was like a toothbrush and brushed them to death. When I got home my mum asked me if I wanted some sweets. I replied 'No sweets bad.' And I lived to tell the tale, even though I'm 60.

William Edwards (9)
Alne County Primary School

A DAY IN THE LIFE OF THE WIZARD NAGOR

I was woken up by my apprentice, young Harold shouting 'It's dragons!'

'Calm down boy,' I yelled, then dozed. He did an ice spell which got me up.

'Rightyo young Harold, this is how you kill dragons.' I poured some baked beans down the dragon's throat, they then exploded.

'Now I'm off back to sleep.'

'With no breakfast?'

He then ate my dust. After eating fried phoenix eggs I sent Harold packing.

'Now I would like you to do a packing spell while I go off to market.'

'This little piggy went to market,' he muttered. I then left after doing an exploding spell.

At market I sold my enemy Nicholas Obbi a fire-lighting potion, two thirds oil, one third gas. On the way back from market I saw Nicholas flying overhead. (Don't try that at home).

After lunch (Minotaur burgers) I saw Harold who yelled 'Thanks for putting this exploding spell on me.' He then exploded.

'My pleasure,' I replied. (He exploded).

I spent the rest of the day being chased by Harold (he kept exploding at intervals). Through the orchard and the kitchen (kaboom) up the stairs, out the window, (kaboom) through the courtyard until I relented. At which time I had mermaid and chips.

'You have expensive tastes,' said Harold.

'I'll sleep to that and everything else.'

Gavin Jackson (10)
Alne County Primary School

A Day In The Life Of A Hamster

If I could be a hamster for a day I would wake up in the morning, come down from the top floor of my cage, have some food for hamsters. Then I would play around in my cage. Then my owner would come and clean out my cage, and while he would be cleaning out my cage I would run and exercise in my ball. Then my owner would play with me for hours. Then I would go into my cage and have a nap. Then I'd wake up and I would see a hamster, another hamster. I would go up to the hamster and sniff him and talk to him in hamster language. I'd say, 'What's your name?'

He'd say, 'Biscuit, what's yours?'

I'd say, 'Fudge.'

I'd show him round the cage and show him where the water was and where the food was and where his house was and all the rules like not to escape and not to bite the owner and a lot of things like that. Then my owner came and put me and Biscuit in two separate hamster balls and we rolled around. Then Biscuit's ball cracked and the cat came in the room. So I rolled into the kitchen and bumped into my owner and my owner took me back upstairs and saw Biscuit and put me and Biscuit back in the cage till morning. So that is my day in the life of a hamster.

Sam Gilholm (10)
Alne County Primary School

A DAY IN THE LIFE OF A FLEA

I woke up this morning soaking wet. Yes, the dog had had a bath. I clung on for dear life whilst the dog stood up. Oh no, I remembered, what happens when a dog's wet? Yes, they shake themselves. As the leader I had to group everyone together.

'Right,' I ordered to the rest of the pack. After I grouped them together we all waited for the earthquake to begin.

We jumped to the nearest hair and clung on for dear life again. Five minutes of this and our legs were almost falling off!

'Right,' said Fred (the youngest of our sergeants) 'I'm bored of all this clinging on, let's go on holiday.'
'Where shall we go? We need a plan,' I said.
'I've already got one.' answered Fred.
'Oh, well done, sergeant, when have you been doing this may I ask?'
Fred started to look guilty, I could tell he didn't want to say, especially as he was supposedly sick yesterday.
'We wait till the dog goes for a walk, then we hop on any dog we meet,' Fred finished his plan with a clap.
The adventure began.

Our dog ran, then sniffed, we jumped with all our might and landed safely on the other dog! We looked around and found another small pack moping about aimlessly. We got back into our new home almost instantly and realised our terrible fate, the vet was here.
The spray was ready. Noooooo!
She sprayed, we ran, she sprayed, we hid . . .

Rebecca Hair (11)
Alne County Primary School

A Day In The Life Of My Dog

Hi I'm Brindy, it's hard to be a dog. My best thing is sleeping, playing and guarding my bowl. I need to guard my bowl in case that big, fat bully Paul, that's Sarah's brother. I love cats, I love Sarah but sometimes I think she doesn't like me because she's always talking about that kitten. I always get very excited if anyone comes to us but my best visitor is Stephen that's Sarah's other brother but when he goes home I miss him but Sarah says its okay. Every time I go for a walk and I sniff the ground because I'm a Springer spaniel. Sue my owner, she always talks to herself. 'I'm like saying, what are you saying woman.' When I get back I like to sit on my favourite chair. The chair where Sue sits and I marked the chair for her. I hate being left on my own. I get so bored so I mark more of the chair then I get told off but Sarah makes it better by giving me a big cuddle. I love this family and I don't want to leave.

Sarah Hancock (11)
Alne County Primary School

A Day In The Life Of A Dog

Hi, I'm Tom and I'm going to tell you what happened yesterday. It all started when I was getting dressed and listening to the radio. Like every morning I looked out the window and saw a bird in the garden. I was looking at it and then it looked at me. As it did, it didn't stop. It was making me feel a bit zitty. A bit later I was out in the garden. I didn't have any arms and had four legs. I looked all around me. I was a dog. I decided to go up the drive and down the lane. I was walking along until I heard something. It sounded like a car. I carried on until a car came around a corner. It wasn't going to stop so I jumped out of the way just in time. I carried on going until I got to the green. I saw Matt, Josh, Matt Holliday and Freddie having shots on the green. They must have been ready to call on me because they were saying, 'I wonder where Tom is?' I ran over and started to play with them but all they said was 'Go away dumb dog.' So because of that I went storming off up the village. When I was about in the middle of the street I thought I might as well go back. So I did and then I saw the bird and the next minute I was in my bedroom. And that's the end.

Thomas Hartley (9)
Alne County Primary School

A DAY IN THE LIFE OF A FISH

There it was the one and only Golden Barb. It was one of the most colourful fish in the tank. As the man scooped the net through the water the Golden Barb was scooped up and it was put in a bucket of water. When the man had gone over to another tank I quickly scooped up the fish to get a closer look at it but before I could I was zapped into the tank. Wow, I couldn't believe it. I was a fish, a real, live fish. I was in a tank with about 5 Mollies, 3 Cories, and 6 Neons. When the man came back his face went white. I thought I put a fish in here a minute ago. He looked up at the tank and saw me. Er maybe I should get some rest. But the next thing I knew I was being swung about, in a plastic bag. When I had stopped being swung about I was in another tank with some totally different fish. I've got to get out of here.

Yes the lid has been left open. Splosh, yes I'm out, wow! Zap, I'm a boy again. And that was my day in the life of a fish.

Richard Reeve (10)
Alne County Primary School

A DAY IN THE LIFE OF DOGS

I was locked up in bed one day when suddenly there was a creaking, the door was creaking, the door was opening. I ran out and waited for food. There was a lovely scent of chicken and turkey. I scoffed it down and went to lie on the grass for a bit. My owner was shouting to take me for a walk. I was wagging my tail and panting. On my walk it was quite exciting, especially when I saw a rabbit. It was hopping in the bales. So I tugged on the lead until it came loose and I ran after it but after a while I lost it. So I carried on walking. Then my owner brought out a ball and threw it for me. I ran after it and caught it. I kept on running through buildings and sniffing hedges. After a while we went back and I was really tired. I just flopped down and went to sleep. When I woke up it was nearly time to go to bed. So I walked to my hutch again and went into my bed. In the morning I heard the creaking, and I ran out and I could smell the scent of beef. So I scoffed it down and went to have a drink. Then my owner called me again and we went for a walk. I saw a rabbit again and I also lost it again.

Robert Wright (11)
Alne County Primary School

A Day In The Life Of Joan Of Arc

I was doing a project on Joan of Arc last year and that was when it started . . .

'Get off my project, you're creasing it, give it back now,' I said with my loud voice.

Hi, I'm Kathryn Wood, I'm 11 years old and believe me it's quite a boring age. If you heard that argument just before that was me and my brother you see I live with a bizarre family. My dad sings *'Oh what a beautiful morning, oh what a beautiful day'*. That is just so embarrassing. My mum just won't bring her head out from her book, my brother thinks he's really tall but he isn't and there's me, strange, strange me. It all started last year when I did a project on Joan of Arc. I was sitting in my chair when suddenly I felt myself rushing up from my seat. I tried calling out but no one would listen. Then I suddenly found myself hit a hard something underneath me. I thought why was everything black? Then I realised that I had my eyes closed. I then heard someone saying 'Joan, Joan, are you coming in for supper?' I opened my eyes and found my mum staring into my face. I shouted out 'Mum! I don't know what happened I was just . . .'
'Don't talk rubbish, you've been here all the time, moving the hay with your father.'
And I said, 'No I didn't, I was at school.'
'School, what's school?'
I then found out that I was Joan of Arc.

Kathryn Wood (11)
Alne County Primary School

A DAY IN THE LIFE OF EMILE HESKEY

'Come on Emile, the game starts soon,' Gerard Houllier said to me pointing over to the dressing room.

'I'm coming,' I said. We were at Villa Park in the semi-final of the FA Cup against Wycombe Wanderers. In the dressing room everybody was getting changed. I got ready. I took my shirt off the peg. Heskey, eight it read. Eventually the whole team was ready and we heard the chorus of *'You'll never walk alone'*. We met the other team as we went to the entrance, we started jogging out onto the pitch in a line, good old Hyypia was in front of me. In the first half we didn't play very well our best chance was by Ziege with an overhead kick just missing the goal. The whistle blew half-time. At half-time we went back into the changing rooms and Houllier shouted at us. After half-time we went back out onto the pitch, there was a loud cheer for us. I had a couple of chances just missing. Then Fowler came on for Owen. Later in the game Babbel got the ball and crossed it in, I jumped as high as I could and I headed it, the ball went in, it was a goal. I ran and skidded on the floor it was one-nil. Then later we got a free kick, Fowler took it, it soared into the back of the net, two-nil! Then they scored. Final score two-one to us.

Tom Williamson (11)
Alne County Primary School

A Day In The Life Of A Hen

It was quite early and I could hear one of the family going out in the car. We hadn't been let out yet but soon we would be let out. All the other five hens were making a racket because they wanted to be let out, then someone came and let us out. We all ran out and started foraging about for grubs and grass. It was nice to eat all the lush grass and then a yummy grub, oooh, and a worm so delicate and tasty. Whoosh, there went the other hen, she was a naughty hen and she always flew out, as a matter of fact I was also a naughty hen so I flew out after her! It was always nice to go after her outside the pen. Just then I saw the lady that fed us. She gave us a box of scraps which the humans had for last night's tea. We gobbled them up. Then I went to lay an egg. Today had been a good day, but really just the same as normal. I think hens should have freedom, and then suddenly I found myself back in my bed.

Freddie Walker (11)
Alne County Primary School

A DAY IN THE LIFE OF A GHOST

Whoo! It's the middle of the night and I can't scare anyone. You see, I'm a ghost but I can never scare anyone!

I live in St Mary's church, in a small village called Alne. Every night I go out into the streets and simply say 'Whoo!' And if I see someone I go up to them and say 'Boo!' But they just carry on as usual.

It's the 31st of October today, Hallowe'en. I can't wait! I mean all those little kids going round trick-or-treating and then I come out and scare them to death!

The reason ghosts like scaring people is because hanging around for the next, mm, ten million years, does get very boring!

I've been a ghost for 100 years and I'm very bored! I've got to fly. Someone's coming.
'Booo!'
See, he didn't do anything!
It's now 8 o'clock and the first trick-or-treaters are coming out. Let's go and see what they are doing, there are lots of kids here.
Right, 1, 2, 3, 'Boo! Why aren't you scared?'
'Because you were my great, great, great, grandad!' said a little girl, 'I like you.'
'So you can see me?' said the ghost.
'Yes, everybody can!'
'But why don't I scare anyone?'
'Because everyone knows you're a friendly ghost.'
'Where do you live?'
'Just in Gale Road, number 24.'
'Great, I'll come and visit,' said the ghost, 'I'll go over there now, but one last thing, Boo!'

Hannah Stroud (11)
Alne County Primary School

A DAY IN THE LIFE OF RACHEL S

I wake up at 7.00, get dressed, brush my teeth, go downstairs and have my breakfast. Watch some TV, go upstairs and play on the computer. At 8.15 I go downstairs, brush my hair, have my inhaler and go to school.

At school, we had to write about a new room in the story of Charlie and the Chocolate Factory then we went into assembly and then it was playtime. I played with Rosie B. Then it was maths (it was easy) and then it was lunchtime. I had a drink, a sandwich, a yoghurt and a cheese string and then it was playtime and I played with Carol. Then it was activities, the green group were doing an experiment. The yellow group were doing their village model, the blue group were painting and the red group were on the PCs (that's my group, it was fun). After that it was music (that was good fun) and then another play and then games. There were three choices to choose from: football, a game of quick cricket and netball and I played netball and then I went home.

I said 'Hi' to my mum and dad and went to watch some more TV. At 4.30 my sister came home and I went on the computer. My mum called at 6.30 saying tea was ready, so I went down and had my tea, played with my stuff and went to bed and dreamed of weird things.

Rachel Stead (9)
Alne County Primary School

A DAY IN THE LIFE OF A KINGFISHER

I woke from my sleep and ruffled my feathers. I live in a nest in an oak tree next to a river where I have a constant supply. My favourite food is salmon, tuna and water insects, yum. Now I am gliding down towards a blue/silver fish moving gently through the flowing water. *Splash!* A struggling, scaly fish called a cod is in my beak. I bite harder and it is dead. After breakfast I head down the river to a small splashing waterfall where I sit, watching everything. Oh no! A hawk. I'm not scared, it is not as fast as me, the mighty little guy. I charge at the hawk and hit him on his side. He backs away and leaves. I fly down to the river. It is time for lunch. After that several tourists see me and take photos. I pretend not to see but I pose, after all, my feathers are the best in town. I swoop around the corner to annoy the herons on the rocks. I flap about and peck and push and shove. After a satisfying supper I cuddle up in my wonderful, warm, feathery nest and fall into a deep sleep.

Hannah Spencer (10)
Alne County Primary School

A Day In The Life Of Guy Fawkes

'Bye darling! Just going to the lead mines!'

Guy Fawkes pressed down the gunpowder in a small cigar tin. Today was the big day. Guy was going to make a small amount of men pay for a big mistake. His wife, of course, knew nothing about this.

'Men, proceed with the plan. A pile of gunpowder over here and a trail leading to the third garden on the left.'

Guy had calculated all of his plans so nothing could go wrong. Little did he know! He climbed up the crumbling steps. The fresh air felt good on his face after being cramped in the wine cellar explaining to the group. They were a dopey lot. He had to explain his plans twice.

Six o'clock, the sun was setting a deep red on the horizon. Frankie and Herbert were arriving, they would be bringing the lighter. Herbert would be look-out, Frankie would be 'chief distracter'. Guy, of course, would light the powder.

'Stand back!' Guy Fawkes lighted the match, the tiny, gold light cast a shadowy light on everyone's faces. The tiny, gold flame went down, *Boom!*

'Oh no, run!' Herbert had just spotted the King coming down the cobbled path. A semi-circle of guards surrounded him. Herbert and Frankie ran, they jumped over the copper fence. They escaped. Guy Fawkes had got his foot caught around a root.

'Gotcha!'

Guy Fawkes life, plan and happiness was ruined, by *torture!* Painful and terribly true.

Rosie Robson (11)
Alne County Primary School

A Day In The Life Of Amy Newton

I was playing in my front garden with my rabbit. He was hopping around in his run when the paper boy came biking past on his bike and threw the paper at me and it hit me on the head. I took the paper inside. I went to show my mum what had happened and who did it, there was a big red mark where I was hit. I went to have a lie down for a while. I went to sleep, I had a sort of dream. It was where I was watching TV when a programme came on and said if you have banged your head in the last few years you can ring our number 01347 8290256 you will receive £1000 to spend on whatever you want, anything I tell you.

Then I woke up and went to have tea. I had chips, pizza, peas and sweetcorn. For pudding I had apple pie with custard. I had a big shower and washed my hair and blow-dried it. When I came down I watched the news and the weather forecast. It was going to be so sunny and very warm. Then I watched Changing Rooms. Then I got quite tired so I went up to my big, warm bed. When I got upstairs I brushed my teeth, I went to bed and read Harry Potter.

Amy Newton (10)
Alne County Primary School

A DAY IN THE LIFE OF A HORSE

Once I lived at a riding school with my two horse friends Holly and Dilly. Oh my name is Chocolate. It was a nice school and lots of people liked me. Hannah rode me. I'm 12 hands and love carrots. But today I went in a box called a horse box. Then we got to this nice farm and that's where I live now. I miss Holly and Dilly but I still like it on the farm.

I'm going to canter today, I can't wait but I don't like Kate Moon riding me because she's too heavy. My best time to go out for a ride is in the afternoon. My colour is pinto and I'm 8 years old. I'm a girl, we're going on a trek later on. I can't wait but then Rosie came running out crying 'We can't go on the trek because of the stupid foot and mouth. It's not near. Oh well, there's always next year.'

The next day it was school and Rosie might be jumping. After school she caught me and groomed me and then got tacked up and then got on, we went round the lane, then we jumped.

Jessica Mavor (10)
Alne County Primary School

A Day In The Life Of A Fish

A flicker of blue and red and there I was, the shiny Neon Tetra. Darting around the tank. Smooth and shiny. I have so many neighbours, platies, mollies, guppies, bleeding heart tetras and two peppered catfish. Twelve neon tetras, angel fish, asiamies fighting fish and gobbies. I catch up with the neon tetras as they head for the air stone. Suddenly every single fish's head goes upwards. I catch a glimpse of fish food and I propel myself to the surface, the slam fighter blocks me. I try again and get the flack. I do this four or five times and get three flakes. Five minutes later everything is back to normal. The catfish seem quite happy with the scraps at the bottom of the tank. The angel fish swim past us and one looks at me very suspiciously but then swims on past our shoal. I go down with three other neon tetras to investigate the 'no fishing' sign at the bottom of the tank. It was kind of white with other colours in it too. I've only got ten minutes left so I'll go up to the surface to be collected by Dennis. Here he is now. I hope I find the wishteller again to turn into something else.

Christopher Kirby (10)
Alne County Primary School

A Day In The Life Of Me, Francesca

8.00am, my alarm goes off for school. I'm in a rush, 15 minutes till the bus comes. I run downstairs and have my breakfast. Rosanna (my sister) and I run down the road, the bus coming round the corner, we run to our bus stop and just make it to get on the bus. Finally I get to school with my friend Rosie (she sits next to me on the bus). Friday, first lesson art, my favourite lesson. Assembly, good achievement of the week. Break, we are allowed on the field. All the year five girls play tig around the classroom. We all come back in from play. Second lesson art again, with our teacher Mrs Walker. 12.00pm time for lunch. Lunch - play. We play tig again round the classroom. English with Mr Bretherton after play. It's an OK lesson. Last play, I can't wait until my best friend Rebekah comes to sleep at my house tonight. Yes! We go home on the bus, back to my house.

Francesca Inchboard (10)
Alne County Primary School

A DAY IN THE LIFE OF LENNOX LEWIS

I was training for my match today at half-past one. I was going to play someone called The Rock. It was half-past one, I had won every belt. So if Rock wins then he gets all my belts. I got my boxing gloves on and came out into the ring. Everyone cheered and clapped when I was coming out to the ring. Then the Rock came out, some people clapped and cheered over at the far end of the boxing stadium. A man called out 'Round One' and a bell rang. The game was on. I swung out my right arm and hit him in the head. Then he did the same but I moved out the way and punched him in the face. We kept doing that and then I blocked his punch and the bell rang, we went to the corner of the ring and people gave me drinks and towels to dab my face. Then the man called out 'Round Two' and we went out to fight. I hit him with my right hand, then my left, he was in pain so I used my left hand and smashed him in his face. He was still up, he had not fallen down yet, so I smashed him in his face and he fell down. I had won the match, everyone cheered and clapped. I kept all the belts and Rock was still on the ground.

Toby Hutton (11)
Alne County Primary School

A Day In The Life Of A Joiner

7.00am
The alarm sounds like a duck, it's so loud, it's like an elephant or a lion bellowing in your ear. Apart from that I had a nice, long, warm shower, got dressed in the usual jeans with a hole in the left knee, a T-shirt with a Kawasaki Ninja. Then I went downstairs and to my surprise there was Simon my oldest son studying, lazy boy he is so I hear, but he was buried in books with the dog whining softly on his knee.

9.00am
I've got to make a very difficult piece of furniture worth a fortune. It's one of the most expensive and complicated pieces, it's a sort of zigzag bookshelf with drawers to support 205 books, that's two times the dog's weight (107 kg).

1.00pm
The lady is not convinced with it I've put all my effort into it. I've slaved over it, now my back is sore, since I started. Now it's time to go home for a rest.

Samuel Hinrichs (11)
Alne County Primary School

A Day In The Life Of The Flintstones

Hi, my name's Bam-Bam, I live with my mum and dad, Betty and Barney. We live in Rock Village, no one lives here anymore because they are scared of Dad. Anyway, I've got to go on my adventures. You can come with me if you want but it might be a bit scary. So hold onto your seats, here we go.

The Jungle Master

We were in the jungle, when suddenly it came. Mum screamed. It was a monkey. Dad had to carry Mum all through the jungle. When we were out of the jungle Dad's phone rang. 'What a good time to ring!' said Dad. We had to go home. When we got home I had some leaf shorts and a T-shirt, so I dressed up as a jungle master with a bandanna headband round my head. I said 'I'm not going to a jungle again.'

Harriet Lund (9)
Arncliffe CE Primary School

A DAY IN THE LIFE OF A NEW SCHOOL

My mum drove me to school and I was feeling very worried. When I got there everyone was staring at me, as I walked through the classroom, except this little girl in the corner, with brown hair. The infants' classroom was being painted so we all had to work in the juniors until play. I had to sit next to two mean year sixes, who kept laughing at me and my work.

At playtime, no one would play with me. I scurried across the playground trying not to notice the teacher, she looked fierce. I looked the other way and saw some children playing a game which looked quite good.

I went over to ask, but it was no good. It was the same as the other children, no infants allowed. 'You're too young, this game's only for juniors.' I turned and plodded away. I felt hopeless. I started to cry. I didn't want to tell the teacher, she looks fierce and unkind and the children might pick on me.

In amazement I saw a girl with long, brown hair walking towards me.
'What's up?' she asked.
'Nothing,' I said in a sad voice.
'Come on, there must be something wrong.'
'Well . . . no one is letting me join in. They say it's just for juniors.'
'Don't worry, come and play with me, my name is Tara. I came yesterday.' she said.
'My name's Fiona,' I told her.
Soon it was time to go in. I sat next to Tara. We chatted together and helped each other with our work. At dinner it was quite scary. If I didn't eat everything I thought I might get told off. But I tried to eat as much as I could.

After dinner I met Tara again. We play with the skipping ropes and balls. At home time I said 'Bye' to Tara and Mum came to pick me up. She asked if I had a nice day? I answered 'It was all right I suppose. At least I met a new friend called Tara.'
'Well, I hope you make more tomorrow.'
And I did.

Fiona Groves (11)
Arncliffe CE Primary School

A Day In The Life Of A Dog

This story is about a dog named Dot and how she gets trained by Megan, her owner and Emily, Megan's best friend.

They take her out. Megan is blind, so Emily guides her. Emily and Megan are trying to train Dot to be a guide dog and well-trained.

One sunny day Megan and Emily took Dot for a walk and a training lesson. They taught Dot to heel, sit, walk beside Megan, stay, rescue people and ignore other dogs.

Emily and Megan took Dot for a very long walk. When Megan and Emily came back from their walk Emily said 'Megan, why don't we train Dot in here and get her to rescue us?'
'Hmm,' Megan muttered thoughtfully. 'Yes, I think that's a very good idea.'
So Emily went into the loft and shouted 'Help, help, oh help!' And Dot came running up the stairs to the loft.
'Good girl for rescuing me,' thanked Emily.
'Teatime,' shouted Megan's mum.
'See you Dot,' said Megan and Emily.
'Yum, yum, tea!' said Dot.

Emily Cowan (9)
Arncliffe CE Primary School

A Day In The Life Of A Lamb

In a barn in the Dales I am watching a lamb being born. It is in a light, fresh barn with lots of sheep. It looks nice and clean and it smells like sheep. It sounds quiet because we have just let the sheep out. One sheep did not come because it was lambing and could not get up.

I tell my dad that the sheep can't get up and he helps the sheep. The lamb comes out and the sheep is licking the lamb. The lamb tries to get up but it tumbles over. It tries again and it gets up. It is sucking and me and Dad put the lamb in a pen with the sheep.

The pen is nice and it has got clean straw in. Dad gave the sheep some hay and food. I gave the sheep some water, you have to give them a full bucket.

James Hall (8)
Arncliffe CE Primary School

A Day In The Life Of A Guinea Pig

My name is Cinnamon and I am a brown guinea pig with ginger spots. I have an owner called Lily, who has green eyes and short blonde hair. She usually wears jeans and a yellow jumper with a flower on.

One day the sun was shining through the slats of my cage and I was looking forward to being let into my run. I scampered out.
Munch, munch! Nibble, nibble!

Suddenly Lily rushed to the run. 'Oh Cinny, Mum and Dad want me to go to boarding school, so we're running away together,' said Lily with tears in her eyes. I was snatched up and we ran off.

Lily carried me for a couple of hours and then we rested under a tree. Lily fell asleep but I decided to explore. As I came out into the sunshine, a large shadow crossed me. I was frightened and fell down a burrow. I landed and a pair of orange eyes rested on me.
'Who are you?' I asked.
'I am a baby rabbit and Mum has just gone to get a cauliflower or two. Who are you?' said the rabbit. Then there was a scurrying noise.
'I'm back,' called a voice from above. 'Is that your friend?'
'Yes,' replied the rabbit.

Mummy rabbit made a fuss of me and gave me some broccoli. Then I said 'Thank you very much Mrs Rabbit but I think I should go and find Lily, my owner.'
'Now Son, be a good rabbit and go with Cinnamon,' said Mrs Rabbit. The two of us set off into the long grass.
'It's ch-chilly isn't it?' My teeth chattered as we scuttled through some trees. After a few minutes the little rabbit groaned.
'Can we stop, my paws are aching?' So we sat down on a clump of grass and began to nibble. Then we decided to go on. The clock struck 5. 'Oh no!' exclaimed the rabbit. 'I promised Mummy I'd be back by 4!' He scuttled off into the distance.

I ran along feeling sad. Then I saw a familiar face in the distance. Lily, she was running towards me. Suddenly she scooped me up.
'Oh Cinnamon I thought I'd lost you!' she cried and burst into tears.

Later that day, Cinnamon woke up in her run. It had all been a dream. Lily gave me a cuddle and said 'I'm going to boarding school because I can take you with me.'

Megan Paul (9)
Arncliffe CE Primary School

A Day In The Life Of A Leopard

Once in India, in the hot Savannah, there was a leopard. Her name was Shadow and she had a sleek, yellowish-brown coat with black spots. She was very clever.

One morning she woke up in her den, in the dense thicket of India. She checked that her three cubs, Moonlight, Glitter and Sparkle were still asleep. She crept out of the den into the tall, wavy grass and trotted away to do the morning's hunting. She caught a baby antelope. As she prowled back to the den, she spotted a familiar shape. It was the old, mean lion, Farla. He always crept in the grass looking for animals for a yummy dinner. Then he would ambush them from behind the trees and take the food away.

Shadow could climb trees and Farla couldn't. She leapt up the tree and took her kill. Farla saw Shadow up the tree and decided not to fight. Shadow jumped down and carried her kill back to the den. When she walked into the den, the starving cubs clambered over the floor to get their share of dinner.

They all tucked in like a pack of wolves. Once they had finished they went for a bath. The babies splashed around. Shadow slipped in and glided around contentedly.

Inside the den Shadow and her cubs were very tired and sleepy. Shadow licked her cubs, then they settled down to sleep beneath the shining stars. It had been a tiring day in the Savannah for Shadow.

Sinead Devlin (9)
Arncliffe CE Primary School

A DAY IN THE LIFE OF A FERAL CAT

The 24th of May 2000 was a usual day on Blackmoor Avenue, but not for Taiko, the Siamese cat. This is why.

That day Taiko woke up next to a drainpipe with water rushing out into a deep, black hole, which ran into a sewage pipe. So the dirty water must have woken him up. Taiko noticed a bush nearby. Something made his eyes bulge out, like snooker balls. It was a *mouse!* Taiko decided to hide behind the bush and pounce on the mouse. Taiko put his plan into action. But just when he was about to pounce on the mouse, his tail hit a thorn bush and he let out an enormous screech of pain. (Obviously, the mouse ran away).

Taiko ran after the mouse. He pounced and caught the mouse. After that he ran into the house where his owner lived. She saw Taiko and gave him some water to drink. Taiko ran into a bedroom and jumped up on a bed and went to sleep. Taiko was asleep for about an hour. When he woke up he ran to his owner for some attention.

He decided to go outside to prey on some mice because he was hungry. When he got outside a big, black cat came into focus. Taiko noticed he had caught a mouse and was eating it, so he knew what he had to do. *Fight!*

A very tiring day.

David Bish (9)
Bardsey Primary School

A Day In The Life Of A Howler Monkey

In the African jungle lives a family of howler monkeys. Today the young ones are swinging merrily, leaving their mother to rest and their father to hunt. As it becomes later in the day, they settle to eat their bananas.

Soon they're having a snooze after lunch. That is, all except the youngest one, who goes back to swinging in the trees. He stays close to his family so he doesn't get lost.

The little howler monkey is still waiting after two hours. Finally his brothers wake up. The small monkey goes back to swinging but this time with his brothers.

Night is falling, so they head back to the tree. Then again they eat some more scrumptious bananas for the end of the day meal. The small monkey sits alone as the sun sets and night comes nearer. The others begin to nod off.

It is darker than ever now but the little howler monkey stays awake. Soon he decides to curl up by his mother. Still with his eyes wide open he shuffles a bit, then is still. About 3 hours later the monkey still has his eyes open staring at the bright stars in the moonlight. Suddenly, as fast as a bullet out of a shotgun, his eyes snap shut, into a deep sleep.

Anna Shindler (9)
Bardsey Primary School

A Day In The Life Of My Grandma

On a typical day, I have time to sit and relax, although on many days I am called out to help poorly pigs on my son's pig farm. My ginger cat wakes me every morning (I brought her in as a stray and she's stayed with me ever since!) and I go down to the bottom of my garden to feed my grand-daughter's guinea pigs. Then sometimes, I walk round the farm to feed a sick pig or, as was last summer, feed the ducks on our pond.

My grandson's dog, Molly, pounces upon me and follows me inside to eat from the cat's bowl. I then slowly make my way upstairs to have a cup of tea with my husband.

Sometimes my youngest grand-daughters will come round. I'm usually found knitting them a woollen clown or making them a papier mâché animal!

Early in the morning I am woken by the squeal of piglets, sometimes being injected. I spend a lot of my time gardening, maybe tending to the rare, sick pig or feeding the fish and newts. I will sometimes walk down to the beach to watch as the gentle waves lap at my feet. Many a time I will walk along the lane and look at the wild flowers.

In the summer, my grandchildren and I make hay dens after harvest. In the winter we build snow igloos.

Living in the country is a blessing to me and so it will always be. Long live the countryside.

Emily Skipsey (10)
Copmanthorpe Primary School

THE LIFE OF A MOLE

It was dawn. The birds were singing and the sun was beaming down onto my mole hill. I tried to bury my head deeper into the crunching leaves and dead twigs, even though I was awake. The light caught my eyes so I decided to get up. I staggered out of my bed, half asleep.

I went deeper into my mole hill so I couldn't see the light. I went to get some worms for breakfast. The mud walls were covered in them. I picked the big, fat, juicy ones first, then the little ones. As I trudged back up the hill, my long, sharp, narrow claws sunk deeper into the soggy, squelching mud.

Back where I live, I ate my worms slowly, wondering what to do during the day. I went for a walk along the hedge-side. I normally did this. I gazed at the golden trees brushing in the wind.

I walked for most of the day. I normally take a stroll down by the meadow. The children were singing and picking daisies and the sun was shining down onto the green, fresh grass. I snuffled along the tall wheat growing and then went in deeper, to find my worms for my supper. I took them back to my hill to eat. After I had eaten my supper, I climbed into my pile of leaves and twigs and I could still hear the yawns of the other moles and me, going to sleep.

Paula-Rae Humphrey (10)
Copmanthorpe Primary School

A DAY IN THE LIFE OF A POLICE DOG

That morning, I woke up really early and was rushed into the van where I had to eat, while the sirens roared. I knew it was an emergency when we drove up to a building blazing fiercely. I leapt out from the back of the van and strolled around the neighbouring streets to keep people out of danger. Then, I sniffed a stranger nearby and I led my master towards the scent. I didn't have much eyesight but my master did.

He grabbed the man and handcuffed him. It was starting to get light by now and the fire was dying out. As soon as we got home we had another call, my favourite job, tracking down a criminal. Same routine as before, racing off to the scene. I immediately started sniffing. A scent! The scent took me all over the town. We did find some criminals but not the one we wanted. Finally we caught up with who we needed; he was breaking into a house. I barked once or twice and he gave in. Then home to doze off to sleep.

Ben Dawson (9)
Copmanthorpe Primary School

A Day In The Life Of Uncle Peter

I wake up, it's Sunday morning so I slowly climb out of bed and look at my watch. It's 9 o'clock and if it's a nice day, I get ready to have some fun.

I go down to the beach and into the nice, cool sea. I go windsurfing because it's my favourite hobby. Then when I come home I usually find my wife, Lynda, getting ready to go to work and my son, Stevie, riding his bike around the garden. Then I play with Stevie for a while, then cook a nice dinner and Lynda comes home from work just in time for her dinner.

If the sea is still nice, sometimes I go snorkelling. It's really amazing looking at all the beautiful fish in all different shapes and colours, so sometimes I stay in the sea for ages. When I come home, I help with the housework and Lynda makes a brilliant tea for everyone and I get ready for the next day when I have to go to work. I am a pilot. I sometimes phone up the rest of my family, who all live in England. I live in New Zealand. I go to bed early for a busy day.

Jennifer Nicholls (10)
Copmanthorpe Primary School

A DAY IN THE LIFE OF PETER, MY RABBIT

My owner came to let me out of my hutch. Being locked in there was not very nice. As I was sniffing some juicy leaves, a cat disturbed me so I chased it through the garden.

It was a typical day, just a bit of digging and sun beaming on my back (that was relaxing). Then my owner arrived to tell me off and get me away from the plants.

There was one that was absolutely gorgeous, light green and yellow. I loved to munch on that one, but it was difficult to get near, it wasn't fair.

I was gasping for some food, my carrot crunches and yoghurt drops. I sprinted to my food. After that I ran to see what was going on at the upper end of the garden. I was sniffing, there was this yellow thing. it was red on top, it looked like a play house.

As I was relaxing in the middle of the garden, I could hear a cat creeping, its paws in the grass, twigs snapping. I chased it out of the garden and onto the fence. It was time to go and munch some plants again. This time my owner didn't realise that I was there because of the bushy bush that is just the right size

Then it was night and I had to go away so I hopped back to my cage. This is the life!

Amy Martin (10)
Copmanthorpe Primary School

A Day In The Life Of A Pencil Case

First thing today I was woken from my nap and filled with sharp, pointy pencils. Then I was shoved in a bag, squashed by some thick paper things and by the time a large pink thing banged me down on a wooden thing, I was totally bruised. A big ringing thing made a loud noise and it was so loud I almost died and went to heaven, but I survived. Then something starting talking and a pencil was taken out of me. After ten minutes, the ringing happened again and I was left half open on the wood.

'You're new aren't you,' said a gruff voice to my left.

'Yes, where am I and what are those ringing things?' I asked.

'You're in school, darling and they are bells,' said a higher voice.

I looked around, on my left there was a lion and on my right, a cat.

Suddenly, the bell rang and I jumped. The rest of the day was much like the first part - more bells and more talking. When the final bell rang, the pink thing shoved me in the bag with the thick paper things. The pink thing took me out of the bag and tried to open me but my zip was jammed. The pink thing cut my end off, tipped out the pencils and threw me in the bin!

I must have fallen asleep because next thing I knew was that I was in a machine that tipped me into a pile of rubbish to be burnt.

Grace Jepson (10)
Copmanthorpe Primary School

46

A Day In The Life Of A Racehorse

The pounding on the door again. I lifted myself up to the window, the sun had already risen. The smell of food lifted me out of my barn. Lovely! As I was plodding towards my food, I saw a strange van taking my friends away. Humph! Over to the food.

Later in the day, I was getting into that van as well. Over the road we went. The bumpy road made me fall asleep . . .

'And number eleven's coming up to the front! Oh no boys and girls, there is a new horse on the track, he is coming up to eleven, he is in the lead. Number eleven is coming up to take it off him. Hey, what's that hurdle doing in the middle of the racecourse? They're both over it, five of them have tripped. There are only seven left. The rest of them are coming round to the last bend, I think we have a new champion. Oh no, number one has taken the lead. Five jockeys have come off their horses, numbers one, two, four, eight and number ten. The new one has won.'

'Wake up, wake up, you and me are gonna win this race once and for all.'

Nicholas Baker (10)
Copmanthorpe Primary School

THE DIARY OF A CIRCUS LION!

I had to get up early this morning. I didn't think you could get up any earlier than I normally do, but you can. It was 3:30am when they dragged me out of bed and hurried me to get changed into a stupid clown's hat and brushed my mane to make it all curly!

When they had finished making me look all girly and silly, they pushed me on stage, but there was no audience. There was just this weird black thing and I heard someone say that they were here to film, but I'd never seen anything quite like it. They told me to do act one and if that took three hours and I had five acts, that would make fifteen hours altogether.

Anyway, when we had finished act three, nine hours later, I was allowed a break. Then my best friend, Milly Minks, the monkey turned up. However, I didn't get a chance to see her because when I was on, she was off and when she was on, I was off.

Lunch was the worst food ever, so my day up until then hadn't gone too well and it got worse through the day, like acts four and five took seven hours each and tea was worse than lunch!

That night I went straight to sleep, dreaming or should I say having nightmares about the next day, for the other lion was on holiday and I would have to take over from him and he had seven acts, all of which were longer than mine!

Melanie McDaid (10)
Copmanthorpe Primary School

A Day In The Life Of My Puppy, Pepper

I had just woken up with a big yawn. My owner had just come down to let me out, oh and Liz, my owner's other dog.

I felt really cross, my owner had just given Liz food and not me. This doesn't normally happen. I felt puzzled as they picked me up and put me on the back seat of the car. I had this funny feeling that I was not going to like where I was going. I was right. They had taken me to the most dreaded place on earth, the vet's.

'Could you please take Pepper through now.'
Where was I going? What was going to happen to me? Will I survive? My heartbeat started to get faster and faster. The vet laid me down on the table. I tried to get away but however much I scrambled and barked, the tighter they held onto me. I tried to stay calm but my anger and worries were too much to keep hidden. I started to whine, then bark, then howl. Before I could think about what I was doing, the vile vet had put a mask over my nose, it made me feel dozy, tired and sl . . . I fell fast asleep.

Slowly and steadily I woke up. I didn't know what had happened to me but I knew one thing was for sure, I didn't feel my normal self. For the rest of the day I slept a nice long sleep.

Eleanor Grierson (10)
Copmanthorpe Primary School

A DAY IN THE LIFE OF A POLICE DOG

I got up and was ready for work. My favourite dog is Blade, he is my best friend and my worst is Sabre. He always teases me because I'm the youngest. The policeman came in and gave us all some food.

Blade and I had to do a job together. We had to bring a criminal back to the police station, he was quite fast but not as fast as Blade and me. Another policeman came in. He put Blade and me on a lead and took us out. In a few seconds Blade and I found the criminal and we jumped on him until the policemen came. We took him away and put him behind bars. Blade said he won't be coming out for a while.

Sabre came up to us and said 'Well done you are very good.'
'Thank you!'
A while later we got our dinner and after that we went crazy outside, then Sabre came up to me and said in a high voice 'Let's be friends.'
Then I simply said, 'OK.'
As we came in Blade, Sabre and I were making new jokes up. Then a policeman came up to us and grabbed Blade, then Sabre, then me, we were doing a job.

Michael Revill (10)
Copmanthorpe Primary School

A DAY IN THE LIFE OF MY TEETH

I wake up to find plaque building up so I give my master . . . toothache!
I can tell when he notices because he starts running to the tooth-fighter.
That tooth-fighter has fought through many battles and has succeeded. I
can see it coming woo-hoo! The plaque is dying and the teeth are
winning.

After the morning fight I usually take a nap, all is silent in the teeth
department. I wake up from teeth heaven, to hear some voices, it is
lunchtime. We still have some warriors from the morning so we use
them against lunch. Some bits of food just get stuck in the gaps
somehow! As we get home, on the odd occasion we get a brush which
is very soothing from half a day's work. By that time we are quite
clean. In another hour or so we get a brilliant brush until they squeak.
All is done that should be done, everything is silent and sparkling. It
sometimes gets misty, I don't know what he breathes but it smells!

Edward Thompson (11)
Copmanthorpe Primary School

A DAY IN THE LIFE OF A BLACKBOARD CLEANER

I have just woken up and I am trying to find my breakfast, which will be broken off pieces of chalk from yesterday's school lesson.

Stumbling over to the floor near the blackboard trying to find my breakfast, I can hear children coming into the building and hanging their coats and bags up as the lesson is about to begin.

I hop back onto the table as the teacher, Mrs Crabapple picks me up and makes me rub out a very long word like alliteration or something. I don't really think you want to know about my life, because sometimes it can be exciting and sometimes it's not, all I do is just sit here on this dirty table and now and again I get picked up and get thrown up and down a blackboard, which gets chalk all in my mouth.

As children start pouring into the classroom the teacher, Mrs Crabapple asks Jessica Smith, the teacher's pet to write the date on the board, but to my horror and by the pain that Jessica causes me I can see that she has put the wrong date on the board and now she is heading towards me nooooo. Spluttering and coughing I try to make myself be seen to the teacher, so she can see how dusty I am and that she washes me under the warm and relaxing tap.

Kate Brown (10)
Copmanthorpe Primary School

A DAY IN THE LIFE OF A CONKER

I get knocked out of a tree very viciously and land on the ground cracking my spiky outer shell, exposing my second shell, which is a lot tougher. Children handle me with so little appreciation for what life is still in me. The child took me away and painted me in nail varnish. I had a really bad stench after that. But that was only the start, far worse was coming. I fear the worst. So this is what my Grandad died of. My mum has told many stories of how, in the autumn, much of the conker population die out in the murderous process of conker fights. Humans just don't have any respect for conkers.

I get a hole pierced through my middle, the pain is excruciating but no way of showing it. Some string then gets threaded through me. Time passes as I get bashed against other conkers, being battered internally. Soon I develop a crack in my shell and I get hurled to the ground, rejected from what seemed a lifetime of punishment. My life does not last long but then again conkers don't live long.

Neil Chauda (11)
Copmanthorpe Primary School

A DAY IN THE LIFE OF A HAMSTER

I woke up to find breakfast waiting for me in my usual bowl. Approaching the bowl, I start to nibble on my favourite food, porridge oats. I was nervous today, because it was my day at my new home. I was planning for an escape, just to explore a bit. I listened very carefully to check no one was watching. I saw my chance, and I climbed up on top of my house and went for the door, but I was a long way off from the cage door. I then thought of a second plan. I climbed up on my exercise wheel, and clung on to the cage bars, but my claws slipped and I fell down. As I recovered, I thought of a brilliant plan! Quickly, I jumped up onto my jam jar, climbed up on the cage bars, stretched for the door . . . and at the worst time possible, a human came in. The human strode over to my cage. First of all, he stared at me then these large hands surrounded me. I tried to jump off the top of the cage, but he caught me and I suddenly noticed I'm back in my cage. Yawning, I shuffled back to my house. Time for sleep. Perhaps I was wrong to want an adventure - where would I find such a cosy bed? Where would I find lovely food? I'm happy in my little house.

Christopher Green (10)
Copmanthorpe Primary School

A Day In The Life Of A Hamster

Glancing around I start to realise where I am. Looking out of my window I can see a fresh bowl of hamster food. I scurry out of my hut and have my usual breakfast and morning drink. Then I look up and see the cage door is open. I don't think I can believe what I'm seeing. I scurry up to the second floor and clamber out of the cage. I look around and see so many buildings staring at me. Suddenly, I hear big footsteps so I run into a building which is actually a piano and then realise I'm free.

Looking around I start to feel scared. Everything is dark and my heart is beating so fast. Phew! My eyes are getting used to the light now. Oh, it's quite nice inside this piano but I would like to get out of here. Help! I start to bang on the piano walls, I can hear people moving about out there. Help me please! Gosh, it is hot in here. Suddenly out of the blue an exit appears. I scurry towards it but then my favourite food sticks out of the exit so I grab on and get put back in my cage and that night I think to myself, *what an adventure.*

James Webster (10)
Copmanthorpe Primary School

A Day In The Life Of A Mouse

Today I woke up, I felt miserable and wondered why, then I remembered the master had seen me in the bread bin. I ate a crumb of stale bread I fetched yesterday from the bread bin. When I was fully awake I crept down after having another crumb and went into the floor under the kitchen. I went up a hole in the ground and stopped in front of the most disgusting looking food in the whole of Skweekville, (my home town). It was almost 12 o'clock and I was hungry. I stopped myself eating it, so I went to my secret stash of food. I saw some mousetraps in the gap near the microwave, a clatter made me jump and my cousin Tim jumped out, looking windswept, from the breeze outside.

He told me to come and stay with him for a while so when I got back the traps would be gone.

A few days later when I returned wearing a new suit and hat my mother was very kind, she packed me some food just in case. When I got back Tim was right, it had gone (the poison) and the traps were gone. Just at that moment I heard a cry of scared panic, it was the master's wife.

Today I woke up!

Jessica Whittall (11)
Copmanthorpe Primary School

A Day In The Life Of A Five Pound Note

Sleepily, I woke up in my cosy money box, sun pouring in through the slit. Yawning, my flatmates ten pence and one penny stretched their sleepy selves. We were just going to have our breakfasts, (sun-dried sunlight) when something or someone blocked out the light. A hand poked into my money box and grabbed me! My heart thumped like a beater on a large drum, so much it hurt! Shouting back to my friends, the human skipped out of the room, firmly gripping me in his warm hand. He stuffed me into a dark rucksack, full of old sweet wrappers and school newsletters. Then the journey began.

The journey was rough and bumpy. It seemed as if I was in there for hours. Perhaps I had, but I wouldn't have known. Finally, the boy came to a halt. He opened up the bag. At last, sunlight filled the rucksack and I could see where I was. A shop! The boy put his hand in the rucksack, and I could tell he was buying something. He took me out of the bag and handed me to a plump lady who carefully placed me in a box. As she closed the lid I could see him leaving, he had bought a toy. I was left in a dark, stuffy box, forgotten.

Emily Fraser (11)
Copmanthorpe Primary School

A Day In The Life Of A Badger

It was morning, the sun was beaming down into my burrow. The leaves that I was laying on turned a golden, reddish colour. I was still dreaming of a warm bed with fluffy pillows, but that dream faded into the distance, I was in the same place with the same smell of mouldy leaves.

I tried to go back to sleep but then I remembered I had lots of work to do. Standing up I noticed the birds playing and the trees blowing in the breeze. It was a warm day, I picked up my bag, I was moving house because of the hunters, they were mean, horrible people. They didn't care about wildlife.

I found a nice spot; muddy and soft. I was not alone. Other badgers and moles and more small animals were building their new houses here as well. I didn't care as long as I was away from the hunters.

Digging was hard work, my claws were getting tired, I had dug for ages and it was nearly ready. My house was ready, this would be lovely! The hunters wouldn't get me and I had new friends. It was getting to the end of the day. Before I go to bed I would have to go hunting for food.

I go round crouching by trees and plants seeing whether food is here. I use my sense of smell to detect where the smell is coming from. Quickly I went and grabbed the food and left. When I got back to the burrow I fell asleep.

Zoe White (11)
Copmanthorpe Primary School

A DAY IN THE LIFE OF A LEAF

As I look out on this windy autumn day I cannot see how I will stay part of the tree for much longer. The wind blows in our faces, tearing our brown, encrusted stems away from the tree. I am dreading the day when I will leave this tree.

Surrounding me now is a whole gust of my brown, crusty relatives. I can hear their distant screams muffled by the roaring wind.
'Help, help,' they shout as they fly through the air.

Just then a great gust pulled me off my branch. As I flew across the field I couldn't help but think where and when I would land. Slowly and slowly the wind died down and, when I finally plucked up the courage to open my eyes I found myself trapped in a hedge. Looking at my body I was nearly sick; I found rips and tears all through my body.

As dark approached the groundskeeper walked outside with his rake and pulled us all into a pile. All I could see as he walked back inside were three children run out from behind a tree and start kicking us around.

Tomorrow the whole process will happen again. A leaf's life isn't very enjoyable.

Joshua Hrycaiczuk (11)
Copmanthorpe Primary School

A Day In The Life Of A Clock

I personally think I'm pretty important but no one seems to appreciate me. All people do is stare at me all day horribly. They pin me up on the wall, believe me that hurts. 24 hours a day my hands go round and round, round and round.

All the way around my clock face I've got numbers. Humans use the numbers to tell the time somehow. I've tried myself but I just can't see them. Well, can you see your ears without looking in a mirror? I bet you can't! Living in a clock's world isn't easy you know, for example, there is a time in the year when they do this thing called 'turning the clocks forward'. Yes, that means me. They twist my nose round and round then walk away. I'm telling you, your life is *much* better than mine.

Once I got smashed and the school teacher took me to a repair man. They were going to just buy a new clock exactly the same as me but they were a bit short of money.

I came back looking brand new. I felt proud. See I told you it's a boring life. This is my story.

Rachel Eastaugh (10)
Copmanthorpe Primary School

A Day In The Life Of A Cat

I woke up. Would I meet my new owner today? Here comes Sid with my breakfast, gobbling it up, I heard somebody walking through the door and heading straight over to me. It looked like I was in with a chance. They asked how much I was, so Sid explained that I was free. So off I went to a new home.

After a short journey I was set free to explore. The door was open, I knew I shouldn't but I so much wanted to. So off I went straight out the house and up the street heading towards the bridge.

It was a hot day, and I was beginning to get tired, so I went up to the bridge and sat on the wall. Suddenly, a big lorry went past and the wind knocked me off the bridge into the river. The water was freezing cold.

A little girl was in a field, she heard me and started to come towards the river. I knew that I would get caught in a big bush coming towards me and hopefully the little girl would be able to save me. She was running after me the whole time. She hurried towards me and picked me up. I immediately began to get warm.

I saw my owners looking for me, they caught sight of me and came running over. They took me straight out of the little girl's arms and took me home to get warm.

Laura Wright (10)
Copmanthorpe Primary School

A DAY IN THE LIFE OF JACK

I woke up at quarter-past eight, and ran to my doggy bowl lying there on the cold, damp floor of the kitchen. I gulped it up feeling very hungry and it tasted better than a normal morning. I had a snooze in my favourite spot then set off to the shop. I slumped in and slept on the floor. I woke up and I knew there was something wrong because Mr Smith wasn't waiting for me on the corner with a scrumptious biscuit. When I got back a cat was in my space, yes a . . . cat in my space.

I chased it off and slept. I went in to find Mr Smith talking to Mary. He praised me with loads of biscuits every now and then. I slept for the rest of the day in my new bed that Mr Smith gave me.

Michael Blenkinsop (10)
Copmanthorpe Primary School

A DAY IN THE LIFE OF A CARTOON CHICK

Dear Mum,
I am sorry to say that I did not make it back to the nest, but Heaven is paradise. I'll tell you what happened. I was on my way back to the nest when the cat from next door sprung out from behind a tree and blocked my way. At first I thought he was onto something, but I didn't realise that something was me. He grabbed me in his paws and would not let go. He put me down on a spoon and tied me up in potato peelings. Then I saw a tin can over a fire and a bubbling mixture which I soon found out was made up of carrots and radishes. A pepper pot and a salt shaker was beside the tin can. Oh and Mum if you think he was getting ready for lunch and he wanted me for dinner, you'd be right. He flicked me into the tin can, started to put salt on and after that he poured on the pepper which made me sneeze. I was scared to death I can tell you. So now you know how I went. Actually it's not so bad, but I do miss you.
Your loving chick
xxx

Joanne Hutchings (10)
Copmanthorpe Primary School

A DAY IN THE LIFE OF A WHALE

Another boring morning as usual. Oh no, he's got the whip, not more practising to do! My wish is to be free like the film I did 'Free Willy'. Being watched by lots of people is scary. The show's about to start, they feed me too much and that's awful. The trainers always stand on me and pull my fins and that hurts.

The show's over and I need to get past that gate. The people feed me, I feel sick. Now I'm just swimming in the pool. I don't like wetting people with my fin, it aches and ruins the show.

The vet comes and checks me every day. I need to be in a small cage for this and I can't move one bit. He gives me an injection. It's really painful, but necessary because I could get a disease from swimming in the same water. They just put the fish in my mouth and it's not the same, because I'm used to catching fish in the sea. I want to get away from Sea World. If I ever get away, I hope I see other whales. I wonder if I could free my friends? Why am I entertaining people and not being free? I was an actor before and now I'm a clown.

I think another show's going to start! This is the part when they pat my tongue. They probably have germs.

Katerina Mina (10)
Copmanthorpe Primary School

A Day In The Life Of A Comma

Earlier this morning I was awoken by a jolt as my friend, the semicolon, was crossed out and moved to the end of a sentence. I screamed as I realised what the sentence was. Well, to be quite honest, it wasn't that kind of sentence. All it needed was a simple exclamation mark! After a few tense minutes, I let out a sigh of relief as teacher came along and semicolon was moved back to his proper place.

For about three hours, everything was calm. Class and young boy were doing maths and I was chatting quietly to full stop when, all of a sudden, I heard teacher shouting at someone. Teacher burst in through the door followed by a figure - the figure was . . . young boy!

He plonked himself down, picked up his pen and started writing. Things seemed to be going well for quite a while. A whole lot more commas and full stops were used and I was happy. I closed my tired eyes and decided to have a nap, after all, I had nothing else to do.

When I awoke, I saw my fellow punctuation marks squabbling furiously with each other.
'I should go!'
'No, last words are always funny!'
'He'll choose me!'
I shrieked as I saw young boy was on his last page. I knew the end was in sight. Just then, the bell rang and young boy ran off. Heavens! Being a comma can be hard!

Jessica Joynson (11)
Copmanthorpe Primary School

A DAY IN THE LIFE OF A SHOW HORSE

I had to get up early this morning and I had just snuggled up in my soft bundle of hay when my owner came. She told me to practise with her around the arena and to do my dressage. This is because today a show is going to take place with lots of people watching us and the judges judging the best rider and horse.

So after I had had some hay to munch and my owner had brushed my thick fawn and white coat she took me out, saddled me up and got on.

This is only my second show and I have been doing it for four years, usually there is another horse but right now he is away doing a show too.

By now I was going around the arena and soon enough it was lunchtime. I had carrots and apples and they were tasty. After I had eaten it was time to go back out again and practice some more, I was tired and soon it would be the show in 30 minutes.

The time went so quickly and it was my turn. I trotted, walked and cantered. I was now feeling as if I was going to collapse, but luckily I didn't. When we got back I went straight to my drinking trough and drank nearly all of it.

I could see the other horse, he was my best mate. That night was fun and I was looking forward to tomorrow because of being with my best friend. I snuggled up once again in my soft bundle of hay.

Amanda Popely (11)
Copmanthorpe Primary School

A DAY IN THE LIFE OF A SPOON

Slowly rusting, the old spoon lay on the floor. Nobody wanted it. It was buckled and bent. All was over for this little spoon. Or was it?

Later that day, two boys came along kicking a tin can. It was the brown-haired and blue-eyed one who saw the spoon first. He picked it up and called his friend over. The blonde-haired and brown-eyed boy came over and tossed the spoon around in his hand.
'Let's take it home!' he said.
The boys collected a number of elastic bands, some small bits of wood and a stand to put it all on. They got to work. First they attached the spoon to a small axle, then they drilled two holes opposite each other on the sides of the stand.

Next they fitted the axle through the holes. After that they stuck on another small stick of wood in the middle of the spoon. Finally, they put on a few elastic bands on either side of the object, from the stick on the middle of the spoon to the stand. They had transformed the spoon into a catapult!

The two boys went to the park to try out their new catapult. They put a stone on the end of the spoon, pulled the spoon back and fired. The stone went quite far and the boys were very pleased. They placed the catapult on the blue-eyed boy's window. The catapult fell down, smashed and rolled away.

Jamie Clark (11)
Copmanthorpe Primary School

A Day In The Life Of A Victorian Teacher

The school inspector walked into the classroom, it was clearly written all over his face that he was in charge.

I shook his hand to make him feel welcome. I could feel my temperature rising, the inspector was holding a long, and what seemed, a heavy cane in his left hand. I was really worried, I could feel the anger of the inspector and see the fear in the children's eyes.

The inspector took a seat, he called out the children's names in order of the register, Jonathan Tinker was the first up. Jonathan was not the brightest of people, if he gets one thing wrong then he's had it.

The inspector started to read some passages so he could write it down even if he didn't understand it. As fast as he could he jotted all these words down. As he went down the register calling out the names, the other children sat anxiously watching in turn.

It's unbelievable how the inspector spoke to some of the children, sometimes they would sit in their place and burst into tears.

Charlotte Issabell was called up to the front. I had a feeling she would do well being the cleverest pupil in the class. But that didn't change anything, the only thing he cared about was being large and in charge! The inspector whipped his cane in front of her and said, 'What's 132 times 9?' She was terrified but then she said '1188 Sir.'

Sophie Wilson (11)
Copmanthorpe Primary School

A Day In The Life Of A Spoon

I just got placed on the cutlery rack. The door slammed shut, it was all dark, water trickled from the plate rack above me. A soft shower of foamy water sprang out of the bottom of the floor . . . 'Arrgh,' I cried, a waterfall splurted out and it soon filled up. I thought I was going to die. I had to get out of there. To my surprise it was relaxing and warm. Later the water started to rise to a terrible heatwave. A friendly face opened the door and I saw light. A smelly hand came and grabbed me and slammed a box over my head. It was transparent with a blue lid. Later on I was on the move shaking about.

Banging against the sides there was a ginger-haired boy about 6. He was the one who put me in a box. He now picked me up and shoved me in a pink cream it was nice. A boy dressed in black asked if anyone had a spoon. 'I do,' said the boy. Look at my strength, and he snapped me, and here I am in spoon heaven.

Matthew Swinhoe (11)
Copmanthorpe Primary School

A Day In The Life Of A Guinea Pig

I was lying in my cage, the wind picked up and rang my waking-up bell. I woke up lazily, my legs felt heavy after a long nap. I scrambled out of my bedroom.

The door was open so I leapt out into my run. I trundled towards my food bowl, I couldn't believe my eyes, there in my bowl was a guinea biscuit. I didn't think and just stuffed it in my mouth. That felt good, I thought as I went to have my breakfast.

After that I went to my food maze, it was easy because I'd done it many times before. Well I wanted to get fat so I kept on doing it about fifteen in total. After, I felt like I had gained four pounds.

Next I decided to try something else so I scrambled over to my most favourite thing, the tunnel. I poked my head in and pushed forward with my rear legs. I felt so excited even though I'd done it more than anything else. I carried on walking, then all of a sudden I couldn't move any further forward! There was only one thing I could do. I squeaked and squeaked as loud as I could. Luckily my owner was there, he lifted me out and put me in the cage. 'I wonder why that happened?' I said to myself as I fell asleep.

Nigel Bancroft (10)
Copmanthorpe Primary School

A DAY IN THE LIFE OF A BAHAMIAN DOLPHIN

Dear Diary

Got up this morning, and had breakfast. Yes, you guessed it, fish and bacon . . . yuck! Next Ozkan my owner came and hosed me down; that water is soooo . . . *cold*! Ozkan then gave me my conditioning tablet so my wet skin would stay smooth and shiny. Ozkan was my favourite member of the Blue Lagoon staff and he always looks after me really well. It was nearly opening time before Ozkan had finished hosing me down.

The humans then crashed through the gates and started to crowd around me. 'Oh no!' I said to myself as I saw a giant near me. She must weight over 23 stone! Well that was it! I played dead and pretended I was ill! I wasn't going to let a big, fat lady jump onto my fin, you can think again! My owner Ozkan then dived in the Blue Lagoon pool as he thought I was actually dying! He came rushing over to me in the water and all the crowd were oohing and aahing like there was a firework display going on.

For the rest of the day/afternoon, guess who was being pampered? Yes, you guessed it, me! Now I think you might know why Ozkan's my favourite member of the Blue Lagoon. The day had nearly ended but before it had I got an extra portion of my favourite food. Fish and pork scratchings.

Cassie Williams (11)
Copmanthorpe Primary School

A Day In The Life Of A Donkey On The Beach

Saturday 17th August:
Woke up quite early, from the shouts of the ice cream man, I mean who would want an ice cream at 8.00 in the morning? I forced myself out of my nice, warm bed and waited for my bossy keeper, I don't know why. My bed's the best part of my job!

As soon as my keeper came, I pushed past him and searched the sandy floors for left-over chips or melted ice creams. That's all he feeds me left-overs! He won't even give me one little carrot!

I slowly trotted towards the long queue for donkey rides. The first few people were kids but the next were, let's just say larger. I felt like I was going to collapse. This was going to be a long day!

Before lunch was the worst. The first little boy, was scared of me and threw his lolly at me. I can still feel that sticky stuff on my body. I was just getting ready for a break when a late customer came! She jumped on my back and I fell over. Then she was complaining for a refund. Typical!

I had a treat for lunch a kind man with a long beard gave me five carrots! The afternoon was quite boring, no heavy people thank God! Most of them were whining kids.

Tonight was one of the best nights so far. The stable was as quiet as a mouse, and very peaceful!

Bethany Cammiss (10)
Copmanthorpe Primary School

A Day In The Life Of A Guide Dog

I was woken by the sound of my old friend snoring. I didn't want to get up but I knew deep in my heart it was my job to look after him. He was all cuddled up to his blanket in his nice warm bed. I knew he was getting old, and he would die soon. I would feel guilty if I didn't give him what he wished for, which was to be looked after until he passed away.

Oh I wish that I was not trained to be a guide dog from when I was little so I would not have this feeling. I'm sure it will bring an empty hole in my body which I could not fill. I'm sure it will just stay there throughout my life.

I knew it was going to be another awkward day like always. Something bad did happen. We were at the bus stop as usual, waiting to cross the road. He started to cross the road. I barked when I saw the car, but it was as if he was meant to die, or even wanted to die. He might have been in pain. I yelped, I could not watch, I could not face my best friend dying. It was all my fault, I should have looked after him.

Rachel Morley (10)
Copmanthorpe Primary School

A DAY IN THE LIFE OF AN INSPECTOR

One cold, frosty morning I was walking to school, I was terrified because the inspectors were coming and they would ask me lots of questions. When I got there I sat down on my chair shaking with fear, we waited in silence, then there was a knock on the door. A big, fat, grumpy man with a long, black cloak came in, he looked awful, he shouted my name out, 'Sindy Mikkle meet me in the hall.' I walked slowly towards the door terrified with fear. I sat on a chair looking at the horrible inspectors. They said, 'What is 8 x 9?'

'Don't know,'I shouted, looking awful.

'Right then, one more question, if you get it wrong you're out,' screamed the inspector.

'What is 6 x 14?'

'Err 220,' I replied.

'What a ridiculous answer, get out you stupid girl.'

I ran out bursting into tears. I ran into the classroom and sat on a chair thinking. I was scared, I ran out the classroom and went outside crying my eyes out. Then it was Rosie Jackson's turn. She came back and got a good mark, then I went back into the hall to see what my marks were. They were OK and I went back to the classroom and told the teacher.

Melissa Lacey (10)
Copmanthorpe Primary School

A Day In The Life Of Echo

Misty gave a purr of relief as she finished giving birth to the last kitten. Through the night she had been giving birth to four beautiful kittens.

One of them by the name of Echo, was extremely adventurous and as soon as he had opened his eyes he was wandering all over the cat bed. He staggered about unsteadily trying to get the feel of walking but not being very successful, so far he had managed to get six steady steps in a row. Eventually Echo could walk about the cat bed easily.

Now he had got the hang of this Echo's new target was to get out of the cat basket. Unfortunately, the rim of the bed was quite high, but Echo had a plan. When all his brothers and sisters lay down together he would use them as steps out. Now he had the plan it was time to put it into action!

When they lay down little Echo climbed up on them and pounced out. He was free! He was so happy that he scampered round the room at top speed. After all that running he heard a gentle padding noise behind him. Before he could run out of the way his mum grabbed the scruff of his neck gently with her teeth.

As she carried him back to the bed he tried to struggle out of her caring grasp. He thought to himself oh well, there's always tomorrow!

Catriona Ferguson (10)
Copmanthorpe Primary School

A DAY IN THE LIFE OF ECHO THE DOLPHIN

Today I just woke up and thought to myself, 'What a lousy night's sleep.' I could already see the strange people queuing at the gates, so I swam over. As all the tourists clambered, they threw in the usual morning breakfast . . . fish! How boring!

At the other side I could see a couple of children waiting, so Flipper and I swam over hoping they weren't as heavy as the fat woman yesterday. All you could hear was screaming and laughing. Finally the ride had finished and then the children ran off happily, but that wasn't how I felt at all.

I wish I had been more careful in the Pacific, it was much more fun there.
'Mmm, I wonder what Misty's doing back home?' I wondered.

My owner, Jordan, came with his new girlfriend, Claudia. Everyone started to leave. Claudia wasn't welcome, she's trying to get rid of us! Jordan threw some fish in, that's all we ever eat around here!

I suppose we should be grateful though, as we had to fend for ourselves in the Pacific. Dolphin Parks aren't the best places to live, but anyway, I've made tons of new friends.

It's midnight now, time to sleep, I need to be up early, Park special tomorrow.

Rebecca Moses (11)
Copmanthorpe Primary School

A Day In The Life Of A Race Horse

This morning I woke up feeling really lazy. I was so tired I couldn't move. Before I could fall asleep again the door of my stable creaked. My trainer came in with his bucket and sponge.

'Come on Istabraque,' he said, 'race day.'

He cleaned me, then put my cosy blanket on. I then found out that I was going to race at one of the biggest race courses, Newmarket. My trainer then led me into my horse box and drove off.

On the journey all I could hear was the noise of the traffic behind me but I could not see anything as I was tied up and could only eat my precious hay. At Newmarket I had to walk round a ring, that was boring. Then I realised that I had Frankie Dettori on me, and he was overweight. Anyway, we galloped to the starting line. We were off, I wasn't quite sure if I could win this race because I thought my legs might collapse. This race was seven furlongs and I was only at the fourth and I was already tired. We turned round the bend to see the finishing line, Frankie whipped me several times, it hurt. I decided to pick up speed, I was neck and neck with Kevin Darley. At the line I had just won by a fraction.

'Now that's what I call a champion horse,' shouted Frankie.

Adam Rollinson (10)
Copmanthorpe Primary School

A DAY IN THE LIFE OF SAM THE DOG

As the sun crept out from behind a cloud, Sam leapt up from his basket and pawed at the bed for the parents to wake up, The parents didn't wake so he barked. The parents did wake up then. After that the two boys woke up shouting 'It's Christmas, it's Christmas.' Sam got excited and barked with them, he rushed downstairs and waited at the door. When the parents came down and opened it for him he sprinted into the lounge and leapt around barking. Then they gave him his present, he jumped around and ran at it and tore the wrapping off. He got it stuck on his head then ran around trying to shake it off but it wouldn't budge. Finally it fell off his nose, the parents thought it was really funny and got it on video camera. He also liked the boys presents as well, especially the chocolate that looked really nice. It smelt nice too. At lunch he got some turkey, he chewed it up and ran upstairs. He wanted to go to bed, he pawed at the door, one of the boys came up and let him in. He ran to his basket and rolled around then fell fast asleep after a long, exhausting day.

Jacob Lilley (10)
Copmanthorpe Primary School

A DAY IN THE LIFE OF A VICTORIAN PUPIL

One sunny August morning, I was walking to school with my best friend, we were talking about the Inspection. I was appalled when I heard what my older friend said about how they treated us.

We arrived at school, I quietly opened the door. Miss Alice was standing at the desk she said, 'Come on, the inspector will be here in a minute.'
Miss Alice took the register quickly. Then the inspector came in. He was very bulbous and round, he shouted at the class, Miss Alice hurried to greet him, she let him sit in her seat.

He asked us if we could tell the time, we said 'Yes.'
He said to me, 'What time is it?'
I said, '9 o'clock.'
'Very good,' he took me into a little room where two other men were sitting down at the side.
He said, 'Now, do you know what the answer is to 22 x 30?'
I said, 'No.'
He said, 'Do your 15 times table.'
It was a shock, I didn't know my 15 times table, but to my amazement I managed it. The inspector said I was very good and they joked saying that they didn't know it, I felt pleased.

Rachael Colclough (9)
Copmanthorpe Primary School

A DAY IN THE LIFE OF A FLUTE

I was sat down comfortably in my case when somebody stuck their sticky, little hands on me. They picked me up slowly and fixed me together, they took me into a room where there were three music stands and three chairs. The person carefully put me on a table.

The next thing I knew someone was blowing into me like a whirlwind. They blew and they blew, I was getting warmer and warmer. Finally, they put me back in my soft, velvet box.

My box was then lifted. I was jolted about. They must have been running because I got a dreadful headache. We stopped, I was lowered and placed to rest for a while. I heard a shout. After an hour of comfort I was off again but this time I was stuffed to the very bottom of a bag.

Eventually I arrived in a very hot place. An engine roared and music played. After about five minutes we halted, I was glad. If I'd been there any longer I would have melted. I knew I was nearly home. Swinging me backwards and forwards the person carried me. I was thrown into a soft bed. Finally, I was underneath it. That was my day as a flute. No doubt I'll be stuck there until next week!

Chloe Marsden (10)
Copmanthorpe Primary School

A DAY IN THE LIFE OF A £1 COIN

I was sitting in a bright, luminous pink purse when a tiny, dirty, sweaty hand grabbed me and put me in a machine with loads of other different coins. I sat there for a while wondering what would happen next. Suddenly a bell rang and lights were flashing. I found myself rushing down a tube into a tray and I landed with a clatter. Another human picked me up out of the tray and put me in his back pocket. As he was running I was bouncing around with other coins. I was exhausted by the time he stopped and picked me up. This time his hand smelt fresh. He gave me to a woman and she put me into a cash register. All of us coins were set out into little sections. I stayed in there for quite a while. Then that cashier picked me up.

'Hooray,' I thought, 'I'm out of here!'

A little boy and his dad bought a puppy, so that's what got me out of there. He put me in his pocket and took me home. His mum asked him for some change and he said, 'I haven't got any I don't think. Let me just check.' He went to look and he gave me to his mum. She put me in a bright pink purse and I thought that the purse looked familiar.

Stephanie Muscroft (10)
Copmanthorpe Primary School

A Day In The Life Of A School Inspector

It was a grey day. Rain was pouring down and thunder was roaring like a lion.

As I walked in the door, a knot formed in my stomach. I was nervous for the school. When I walked in the classroom stiffly, the teacher shook my hand with a tight-lipped smile. I quickly glanced at the pupils. They all looked scared to death.

I was seated on a little wooden chair near the small round glass window.

'You,' I said to a small girl with sunshine yellow hair and chestnut brown eyes, 'what is 5x8?'

'40 Sir,' she said, almost a second after I had asked her.

Then I pointed to a medium-sized boy.

'What is 6x6?'

'36 Sir,' he said.

I carried on like this until I had pointed to every pupil. I must admit I was pretty impressed when I was finished. Next was English.

I reached into my red leather bag and pulled out a Bible. A little boy's lip suddenly began to quiver and quake. Tears began to spring from his eyes and dribble down his cheek. I was very angry but I didn't show it. Instead, I smiled at him. Then I began to read.

Some of it was very hard but they managed to get through their writing test.

From then on it was a quiet, easy day. I don't know what else to say, except that the school passed with an excellent mark, even Eddie (the crying boy).

Sarah George (11)
Copmanthorpe Primary School

A DAY IN THE LIFE OF A SCHOOL PUPIL

As I walked to school I couldn't help feeling nervous as the inspector was coming. I knew all my tables and the teacher said I read very, very well. The only thing was that my handwriting was awful.

My teacher was Mrs Smith. She was the nicest teacher in the world and she helped me a lot. I could tell she was nervous.

As I stepped inside I heard people crying. Mrs Smith told me to go and line up. She had a very tight dress on and a Bible in her hand.

It was me next. Rosie went all shaky and ran off crying. Then it was Victoria's go. 'What's 5x9?' '45,' said Victoria firmly. It was me now. The inspector shouted out, 'What's 12x8?' My mind went blank. '96' came out. Well done! Next reading. I whizzed through my reading test. The next test was the one I was dreading. The writing test! Mrs Smith was praying in the corner. I knew I must do this for her.

I felt pleased with myself for doing the test well.

I knew I was moving up a class. Maybe I will find that class too hard.

Amy Ryder (10)
Copmanthorpe Primary School

A Day In The Life Of Nipper

On Sunday morning Nipper woke up lazily and as usual he stretched. Nipper padded across the house to get to his doggie bowl. He slowly licked out all the biscuits he hadn't eaten for supper. Just then my dad noticed that Nipper was panting more than usual. On our last visit to the vet they said that if Nipper was panting a lot, he would have to be put down.

Nipper was now a poorly dog and he had a tumour as well. Dad realised that we needed to visit the vet. He knew what was to happen. Dad woke the family to tell them the bad news. He said it would be better if we - me, my mum, Clare and Steven - stayed at home.

When my dad got to the vets he stroked and patted Nipper for the last time. Nipper looked at him with soft, moist eyes. The vet gave Nipper the injection and he fell quietly to sleep. That was the end of Nipper.

When Dad came home we all wept, apart from my mum and dad who put on brave faces. I stormed to my room and cried into my pillow just about all night. I hardly slept. Nipper would be remembered forever. We haven't replaced him yet. Maybe sometime we will.

Emma Coates (10)
Copmanthorpe Primary School

A Day In The Life Of A Victorian Inspector

I walked into the first classroom, my Bible in one hand and my cane in the other. The children were all at separate desks with their chalk and slates at the ready. The teacher greeted me and took my hat and coat. I shook his hand, then opened my Bible. I read them some passages that they had to copy as best they could. Suddenly a boy burst into tears. I wasn't taking this, so I yelled, 'Get out you worthless swine!' I carried on with the passage, now very angry. 'You'll pay for this you imbecile, you're supposed to teach your children to work, not cry,' I said to the teacher.

I walked towards the door, picked up my hat and coat and turned towards the class. 'I'll be back,' I said.

I walked into the next classroom. Once again the teacher took my coat and hat. I shook his hand, then started to pace up and down the rows of children. I saw a little, wimpy-looking boy and asked him, 'What's 24x5?'

'Um, I'm not sure sir.'

'What do you mean you don't know? Stand up and tell me the alphabet.'

'A, B, C . . . ' and then he just burst into tears.

'Go into the corner and wear the dunce's hat.'

The boy walked there, his head hung low in shame. Luckily, the other inspectors had the job of taking the children into rooms on their own. I just inspected their literature and manners.

We left the school unimpressed.

Matthew Featherstone (11)
Copmanthorpe Primary School

A DAY IN THE LIFE OF A MACHINE

It is 8am and the sweet-making machine has been going as it is now for over 10 years.

Sugar (a large quantity), fats, E numbers, flavourings and much more are tipped into a huge bowl. One of the machine's hands grabs the bowl and at great speed mixes the ingredients together. After a while this sticky mixture is poured into a large tray of oval moulds.

When the mixture is tacky, an enormous hand comes down and, with no sound at all, lifts one part of the tray on top of the other. Two great big hair dryers come down and start to blow on the moulds. The top of the mould is peeled away and inside there are some beautiful green sweets. The second part of the tray in turned upside down, tapped and then lifted to reveal lots of green, perfectly shaped sweets.

As the conveyor belt moves, another tray is emptied of the green sweets in the same way. At the end of the conveyor belt, a box is loaded with the sweets. Each time a box leaves the great room, the machine seems to be waving goodbye to the sweets it has slaved over for hours.

Jenna Partington (11)
Copmanthorpe Primary School

A DAY IN THE LIFE OF RUSTY AND ARCHIE

As the sun sneaked across the sky, Rusty and Archie, the brave hounds from Scotland, yawned and stretched their strong legs. They raised themselves energetically and bounded up the steps of the local park. They were hungry, so they went over to the butchers. Rusty went into the shop, walked over to the man and bit his backside! The butcher, of course, wasn't happy. He ran after Rusty. Archie ran into the shop, grabbed some sausages and pelted back through the door. Rusty came haring back to him and they walked off with the sausages.

Later on they saw a man with a sack under his shirt. He was following an old lady with a handbag. Rusty and Archie decided to follow him. Then the man punched the old lady and ran off with the handbag. Rusty ran after the man and Archie sped towards the police station. When he got there he said, 'Quick, a man's stolen a handbag!'

But to the policeman it was just an urgent bark, so Archie bit his trousers and the policeman ran after him.

'Good work,' said Archie. 'That wee lady will be alright!'

The policeman just heard a triumphant bark. The man was taken to jail.

Aaron Dixon (10)
Copmanthorpe Primary School

A DAY IN THE LIFE OF A FISH EAGLE

As a dark thunder cloud crept over South Africa, a huge fish eagle soared over the clouds.

The huge male eagle dived down, he was not right above a flamingo. Then he caught sight of a fledgling trying to take off for the very first time in its life.

The powerful bird came crashing right on the back of the fledgling, causing sudden death. Dragging the victim to land took some hard work. Returning back to his mate and the nest with his prey.
The one tiny egg lying in the middle of the nest started to shake, as a tiny head and body rose out of the egg. The mother sheltered the baby and it ate some of the flamingo.

Suddenly the sun began to creep up, soon a lovely rainbow appeared on the horizon. The male flew off again to collect some water for his new family. It was hard work because the closest lake was a mile away. He returned with water and a fish. He landed on the nest with a huge thud. Then the sun sank down as the day came to an end.

Anthony Parker (9)
Copmanthorpe Primary School

A DAY IN THE LIFE OF A GUIDE DOG

I woke up this morning to my dreaded alarm clock. Then I went to look out of the window. Luke would have boiled up in a fleece.
Next I went to make our breakfast of toast and marmalade, mmmmm. At 8.00am I went to wake him up, I guided him down his chair lift and got him dressed. The toast popped and Luke buttered it, then we sat and munched our toast.

At 9.00am we walked to school. I was on my lead and waiting to cross the busy road, with cars screaming past. The school was on the other side.

Behind me Luke was putting his hands over his ears, he hates crossing roads, so I have to guide him carefully. After a while the road fell silent and we crossed. I let him walk into the playground on his own to make him feel normal. Then I made my way home.

The Headteacher always drops Luke back after from school. He will be here soon, and very hungry. I am not so good at cooking, well no dogs are good at cooking.

Tonight, I am trying to make a sandwich. Luke won't be back from his weekly Braille lesson till later on so I've got plenty of time to make it.
Luke is back now and upstairs getting changed on his own I am pleased to say. I have triumphantly made him a tuna sandwich. We sat outside in the moonlight and ate it, the moonlight closed in on us like a silvery sheet.

Luke Robinson (10)
Copmanthorpe Primary School

A LETTER FROM MOLLY MINKS

Mr & Mrs Minks
3rd Tree House Way
Jungle Village
Y069 9XD

Dear Mum and Dad,

I miss you loads!
Guess what? I found a job. Are you proud of me?
I am a circus monkey, it's cool. They're giving me lots of food. You can even get dressed up in funny suits. The only bad thing is when I had an accident yesterday I had to clean it up myself, it was horrible.

My room is wonderful, a pink comfy fluffy bed and a wooden bedside cabinet. My fur is brushed every day. Tomorrow I'm going to be shot out of a cannon. I'm frightened to death. Never mind, I have found a new friend - a lion called Roary he is my best friend now.

I have a clown's outfit (it's a bit big though) and I've got a hat with a point on the top.

Love Brogan.

Brogan Bell (10)
Copmanthorpe Primary School

A Day In The Life Of Police Dog Spike

I woke up in my rock-hard bed . . . well, the floor.
Then I heard the keeper rattling the keys, I dread that sound.
'Get up!' he shouted.
I realised it was 'funday'.

I thought to myself, I'll rip that dummy apart. We went to the cooking room, the cook was terrible, we all wished he would get some different food.

Then we were out onto the field, I put one paw outside and almost froze. It was very cold. I saw the red dummy in the fog. I ran straight for him, damn I had a choice lead and that was my last go. I went back into my dirty kennel.

Ryan Whitehead (10)
Copmanthorpe Primary School

A DAY IN THE LIFE OF A COIN

I am money and I was in a purse, well actually it was quite comfy because it was lined with leopard fur.

I had slept on it all night and in the morning I wobbled, I thought oh now, it's spending time.

I hoped that all the one pound coins would be spent first and not me, I'm worth more than they are! I am the lovely two pound coin.

I have been here for three months, suddenly I felt a sweaty hand come in, then the hand disappeared. The purse tipped upside down and I fell out, crashing into all the other coins.

The sweaty hand picked two one pound coins and me up. Oh no! She's put us back into the purse and carried us off. You could tell that person had jumped out of her front door because she shook all over the place. Then we heard a slam and the car engine started then we all drove off.

The car halted, the purse fell off the seat and I hurt myself. Somebody leaned over and picked us up and we were carried out into the open air but just then we were dropped into a muddy puddle. It all started to come through into the inside. I was fed up being inside there, it was uncomfortable and wet.

When we were in the shop, I was put into the till, it was so comfy.

Kathryn Richardson (10)
Copmanthorpe Primary School

A DAY IN THE LIFE OF A CIRCUS ELEPHANT

Ouch, that'll be the circus keeper! I wish he'd leave me alone. I'm tired, you mean thing, just go away. Okay, okay, I'm up. Don't make me wear that stupid piece of cloth.

It's time for the five o'clock show, so stop your wriggling you silly elephant!'
Oh no, not the five o'clock show, that's when all those little ugly things ride on my back! Oh I wish I hadn't gone in that trap, if I hadn't I'd still be in Africa with my family. Well, I suppose that's all in the past now. I'd better get on stage before they start using the whip. Ow! My ears. I hate that applause. Oh and look at that queue to go on my back! Here comes the first one.

Ah! Finally. The last one. Just a minute, what's she doing? What's she doing? She's handing the keeper some sort of paper. Where's she taking me?
'Bye Elsmouth, you've been bought for one thousand pounds, you lucky thing.'
Did I just hear what I thought I heard? I'm leaving? I wonder what that is with four round things and a long red thing on top?
'Here's the house you're going to live in.'
I looked at the red thing.
'No, not the bus, the house.'
I looked to where she was pointing and saw a gigantic thing she called a house. By now it was too late. She took me inside into a room that looked like a jungle. I felt like I was home and snuggled up to sleep.

Jasmine Khouja (10)
Copmanthorpe Primary School

A Day In The Life Of A Laboratory Animal

I've been dragged out of my cage and it's four in the morning. I am carried because I'm too tired to walk out of my cramped room to the noisy experimental room.

My keeper's walking in big strides making me want to faint. We're here! Through the tall blue door. Ouch! I've just been dumped on the cold stone table. My keeper has left but here comes my awful experimenting keeper. What have they got for me today?

Oh no, not the shampoo! They test this in my eyes, it usually stings my eyes so badly, I think I'm going blind. When they've finished with me, I get three bananas.

Oh here it goes! The shampoo is coming closer to my eyes. Ouch! Help! My eyes are stinging so badly, somebody give me a towel!

Ahh that's better. It's dark under here, it helps my eyes. Ooohh, they've taken it now, but it still stings a bit though. My bananas. Yum, these are delicious. Any chance of some more? No! Oh well!

I'm getting tired, I'm going to sleep in my cage. Ahh, my keeper. Oh no, not the big strides again, it's cold in this corridor.

Hey I'm outside. Yeah time to play, this is fun. Ow, I've just got a rope burn, it really hurts. I can't do anymore. Oh good, my keeper's coming to pick me up for tea. The corridor's cold again.

In my cage we go.
My tea, yuck! I'm going to sleep without any tea.
Night!

Eleanor Noble (10)
Copmanthorpe Primary School

A Day In The Life Of A Shell

I was sitting at the far side of the beach where the sea was gently lapping up beside me, pushing me backwards and forwards. It was a lovely bright day and many tourists had come on to the beach.

Lately, I had had a hermit crab living in my shining beautiful shell and it had only just moved into a bigger one because it had grown ever so quickly. My danger then was that with no sea creature in me, children would pick me up.

I was right! I was picked up by a child about three years old and thrown into a small patterned bucket, full of many other shells. After a bumpy ride we were gently placed onto a seat. There was a wheel in front of one, then there was a bang as the three year old and her carer joined me.

With a chug we were off, we were moving. I didn't know where we were going or why these people wanted me. All I knew was that I was in danger of breaking. A crack appeared. I felt my life slowly draining away, but I soon felt as light as a feather, I was floating upwards. I saw an angel.

'Is it true?' I said to myself.
An angel welcomed me into shell heaven and showed me to the beach. The water once again was lapping up beside me. I was at home and there in front of my eyes I saw the rest of my family. I was so happy.

Florentina Plummer (9)
Copmanthorpe Primary School

A Day In The Life Of A Victorian Inspector

As I walked into Grenwich Primary School I felt a chill flow across the yard. All the children stared at me with horrified pinched faces. I ignored them but I couldn't help feeling a strange chill go down my spine.

Inside I met one of the teachers Mr Roberts. He greeted me with a curious look as if he wanted to interrogate me. I smiled at him and he gave me a strained smile back. This made me feel uneasy, so I went to find the headmaster.

I found him in his office playing his shiny gold saxophone. When he heard me knock he stopped playing and opened the door. His name was Mr Johnson, we had a little chat and I asked him to show me the attendance registers. He gladly did, but I noticed a scared look in his eyes. The registers were all perfect, except one - Mr Roberts' class.

I visited them first. Mr Roberts' class held thirty one children, but today, only twenty one had turned up.

I was appalled, Mr Roberts was in disgrace, I didn't even bother to test his class, I was so appalled.

When I tested all the other classes I was very pleased. Mr Roberts was eventually sacked because of his bad class attendance. I have to admit . . It was only Mr Roberts' class that had let the school down, it was mostly the same as every other school!

I wonder what I'll find tomorrow.

Martin Durrant (11)
Copmanthorpe Primary School

A Day In The Life Of A Leaf

I leave my tall proud tree, falling helplessly to the cold ground. Waiting patiently, I hope for some wind to help me to the top branch where I belong with the rest of the green leaves that still remain. There I lay, just curling and twisting through the fresh autumn breeze wondering where the autumn air will take me next; but as the wind has a pause, I hurtle down to the ground.

There, a gang of caterpillars are in search of food. What will they think if they find a big leaf? Will they nibble at me frantically or will they eat me slowly? I don't know! All I know is that my fragile body will be gone and all that's left is a memory of one tiny leaf.

Cari Jones (11)
Copmanthorpe Primary School

A DAY IN THE LIFE OF MY DAD

The day passes by without me, whilst I sleep soundly, the birds and the sun begin to pour through my window.

I have to get up at half past one in the afternoon, take a shower, have my breakfast and get freshened up for the day ahead.

I travel in my car to work at Rowntrees. When I get there the noisy factory hall echoes around me. People began to shout when they need me because I fix the machines, you would be surprised how many breakdown.

It's always long and hard work. The world could be blown up by a bomb but I wouldn't know. It is very isolated inside the factory and when you're hard at work you can't see out of any of the windows.

I do an eight hour shift with only a few breaks. At about half-past nine I ring my daughters but I can't talk for long because I may still be needed, but I'm only a temporary contractor.

Checking my watch regularly, the day comes to an end and finally at 11.00pm I leave for home. When I get home I never want to go to bed because to me it still feels like the daytime. So I usually make myself a snack and then watch some TV, but once I start to feel tired I go straight to sleep.

Vicky Burgess (11)
Copmanthorpe Primary School

A Day In The Life Of A Hedgehog

Slowly, sleepily I wake up from my long winter's nap.

I yawn a huge yawn and shake myself up, scattering leaves everywhere. Everything is calm as I creep out of my burrow and all I can see is a blurred vision of the road ahead. Cars are whizzing past, not giving me a chance to cross.

The coast is clear, I see my chance and quickly scurry across the road. I know many other hedgehogs who haven't made it across.

Now I have to find some food for my family (they're still asleep).

Aagh! I see some nuts over there, I'll go and get them. What's this on top of me, some kind of box? Someone has trapped me. Let me out! How am I going to get home?

Now they're lifting me up and they're taking me somewhere. But where? I want to be back with my family, not in a cramped box in a car in the middle of nowhere. How could they do this, I'm just a poor little hedgehog?

I've been let out and I can see the road and the glorious leaves. Rushing home I wake the family and share out the nuts and I tell them about my dangerous mission.

Timothy Godfrey (10)
Copmanthorpe Primary School

A DAY IN THE LIFE OF A VICTORIAN PUPIL

As I walked into school my knees were shaking because it was Inspection day. I was the first in the classroom, because if you were late, the Inspector would shout at you.

Five minutes later everyone was in the classroom and we heard unfamiliar footsteps in the corridor. It was the Inspectors! Then the door slammed. Suddenly as it flew open, there standing blocking the light we saw three Inspectors 'What's seven times thirty-two boy?'
'Er 224 Sir' said the boy on the front row.
'Very good boy.'

Then the teacher took the Inspectors' coats and hats.
'You, the one on the back row. How do you spell *difficulty?*'
'Er d I f f I c u t y'
'That's incorrect. Get out!'
'Now let's get on with the tests' he said.

I was the first to go, I was taken into a room and asked lots of questions. I answered, still very frightened. They asked me hard questions for example, what's thirteen times six? That's hard! Now I was back in the classroom and we had all had our tests and we were all nervous. We were just about to find out our test results. The first names they mentioned had passed.

Then they said 'Edward Noble.'
I waited, holding my breath. the silence seemed to take forever!
'Pass!'

Edward Noble (10)
Copmanthorpe Primary School

A Day In The Life Of A Collie

I got up feeling very energetic and ate my breakfast, in fact I wolfed it down. Ran to the farmer's door and barked my head off. It must have taken five minutes. Yes, five minutes for him to open the door! But when he did, the wait was well worthwhile because he gave me what looked like the biggest bone in the world.

So off to work we went. Not silly old sheep again?
'Ellie!' the farmer shouted, 'round 'em up!'

This was my favourite instruction, being told to chase sheep. Off I went, round the field up the hill and across the track and into the other field. When the farmer called me back, I fell asleep in front of the fire. I was dreaming about entering the Sheepdog Trials.

I dreamt I went in fifth and in the end I won a giant trophy and a rosette which the farmer stuck to my fur.

When I got up I was shocked to find that there was no rosette and no more trophies in the trophy-cabinet. I soon got up and I went to the food bowl and had tea. Yum, yum, it was my favourite meat, chicken with jelly.

After that the farmer went to bed and turned the lights out, after about twenty minutes I was asleep again.

Chris Kew (10)
Copmanthorpe Primary School

A Day In The Life Of My Mum

At seven o'clock I am ready to get up for a hard days work ahead of me.
I wash my hair and have a quick refreshing shower to start the day off.
At eight o'clock I am ready to set off for work. When I arrive at work I
open the door and turn the light on, then I go upstairs and put my coat
and bag away, then the people I work with arrive and we all put all the
new stock onto the empty shelves.

At nine o'clock we are ready to open the shop to all the customers
queuing outside. It is a hard job keeping the shop tidy and the customers
happy.

At five thirty we are ready to shut the shop and I'm looking forward to a
long soak in the bath.

Lauren Spence (10)
Copmanthorpe Primary School

THE DAY IN THE LIFE OF A VICTORIAN PUPIL

As I walked in the school gates I could see that everyone was as nervous as I was.

Instead of the usual noisy busy playground, it was filled with huddled groups of children murmuring quietly. All waiting for the school bell to go. Eventually after what seemed like hours, the bell rang and we all filed in as quiet as mice.

In the classroom as the teacher handed out our chalk and chalkboards, the Inspector started to read a passage of non-understandable words for children of our age. After that he started firing questions at us, like he was shooting all of us dead.

Then came the worst bit, I was taken to a small box room where I stood in front of three bald-headed men with my teacher behind me fiddling with her dress. I was fired questions again on all different subjects, then they asked me the one question which I had never come across before, it was . . .
'What is 316 quadrupled?'
As it reached my ears, a hard stern voice inside my head told me it would never get the answer.

I came out and went back into the schoolroom. I sat and thought - will I go to the top or have another year of humiliation and doom?
I trudged home slowly, leaving all my school troubles behind.

Victoria Bishop (10)
Copmanthorpe Primary School

A Day In The Life Of A Victorian Pupil

I walked slowly up to the school gates, the cold wind blew damp shrivelled up leaves across the courtyard. When, from the corner of my eye, I caught sight of a very grand looking horse-drawn cab. Oh no! It was inspection day! I stood and stared at the cart for some time, the horses stared back at me but they had a cruel look which made me shiver. When all of a sudden I heard 'Lucy don't stand there, get inside at once!' It was my teacher.
'Yes Miss.'
I ran past the gates and up the cold wintry steps.

As I came into the cloakroom I slammed down my satchel and ran into class. Phew! The inspector wasn't here yet. I quickly collected my slate and my chalk and I sat down.

In the distance you could hear the inspector's voice shouting wildly at the teacher.

'Your class is a disgrace! Get them sorted out, especially Elizabeth!'
Boy that was scary. Oh no! I think he's coming this way. You can hear his shiny black shoes clomping on the stone floor. Suddenly there was a loud knocking on the door. 'Come in,' my teacher said shakily. The inspector came in and stared harshly at us. He walked steadily to the front, there was a cane in his hand.
'You! What is 9 x 8?'
'72 Sir' said a young girl at the back.
'Very good!'
'You! What is 10 x 10?'
Oh no! He was pointing at me.
'Um 100 Sir,'
'Very good, well I'm impressed with this class Mrs Hardy. that's my job done for today. Class dismissed.'

Whoa! I didn't think I'd do this well. Anyway I grabbed my bag and skipped cheerfully out of the school.

Lauren Fox (9)
Copmanthorpe Primary School

A DAY IN THE LIFE OF A BUS DRIVER

I wake up to the smell of my clean bus driver's uniform and the sound of Terry Wogan's voice on Radio 2. I drag myself out of bed and go into the bathroom.

I look at myself in the bathroom mirror- I look grey. I shaved and cleaned myself until I was glowing. Looking at my watch, I panic, I have to take the children to school in half an hour. I ran downstairs, buttoning my shirt. I grabbed two slices of toast and jump into the car. I didn't have time to say goodbye to the children or my wife, so I left a note.

When I got to the bus park I went into the office to pick up my map, mints and air freshener. I looked at the first people on my list and as usual it was the school, it was the children in Copmanthorpe.

They all amble onto the bus showing me their bus passes and taking out their personal stereos.

I herd them off the bus and they hide their personal stereos as the teacher watches them like hawks.

I leave the school to pick up the old people for a trip to the seaside. I turn Radio 2 up, but they shout 'No! Not that old rubbish. Radio 1. Radio 1. We want something new!'

We stop off for a toilet stop and we ended up buying nearly everything in the shop. Finally we get there, they all give me their thanks.
Why? I'm only driving a bus, but deep down inside I know that this is the best job in the world.

Aimee Hirst (11)
Copmanthorpe Primary School

JAGUAR (NOT THE CAR)

Another day in the hazy jungle and another hard working day.

I started pouncing across the jungle. I felt as if my stomach was going to burst. Suddenly a small dot blinked across my eyes, I started chasing after it. It became clearer and my eyes lit up like flames, it was a wild boar. My legs turned to jelly, but I ran like lightning. My mouth dribbled like a river as I got closer and closer and finally it turned into a life or death chase.

I pounced . . . the boar's tail swished like a pendulum from side to side. I clicked my claws out like daggers firing out of fur. I slashed out at the boar's swaying tail and I heard something rip, the next thing I knew the boar wasn't standing on all fours anymore. Then suddenly out of the darkness came three giant leopards with their pups. I thought I was in for a big scrap for the boar, but the leopards had other ideas. They scampered past me and charged after a lion instead, he was probably tormenting their pups.

I decided to go back to my den. The sky was falling fast and the stars gleamed like pearls and my eyes felt heavy.

Matthew Stevenson (10)
Crowlees CE(C) J&I School

A Day In The Life Of Logie Baird

I live in quite a big house and I want to be a famous scientist. A lot of scientist's dreams are to become world famous and I am trying to become world famous by making something ingenious.

I know now what my project is going to be, I want to project an image onto a screen. I want to entertain people with my invention (over 6 years). I think I have finally cracked it!

This is how I'm going to make my invention:

First I will put a puppet head in front of two spinning discs, behind the spinning disks I will put a camera. The camera will be able to see the puppet's head through the two spinning disks. The camera will be connected to a transmitter. The transmitter will turn the picture into radio waves, the receiver will receive these radio waves. The receiver will be connected to a light bulb. The shining light from the light bulb will shine through the holes in the disk. Then a puppet head will appear on a screen. People will be able to sit down and watch puppets on a screen.

This is my invention and I hope it will make me world famous.

Daniel Conway (10)
Crowlees CE(C) J&I School

A Day In The Life Of A Leopard

A ferocious snarl ripped from the leopard's throat. It was stalking a herd of forest deer. The supple and muscular body prowled back and forth on the moss-coated limb of a tree. A strike of gold against the lush green sparkling emerald of the jungle.

Its slitted eyes glared in anticipation at the lithe bodies of the deer, and it took up its predatory stance. Using all its skill and guile, it melted like a wraith into the undergrowth. Then in a fatal leap that would determine whether the leopard would have a feast, he tore through the sun dappled foliage and landed with a thunderous roar on the back of a stag. Minutes later it lay leisurely on top of a rocky outcrop, gobbling succulent chunks of venison.

Dusk descended on the tranquil forest like a falcon. The leopard stood like a statue beside a tropical lagoon. Water tumbled and rolled; plummeted in cascades of pearly blue, in the form of a pulsing waterfall. Hazy mists twirled and played on a sweet afternoon breeze, while the leopard slaked his thirst by lapping up the calm clear water. When his thirst was quenched, he contented himself by dozing in his favourite tree, but he didn't know he would soon be in for a rude awakening.

As swift as the breeze, a second leopard slipped into his territory and began gulping down the precious life-giving water. The first leopard stirred in his sleep, then opened one eye. The single eye scanned the area, and when it rested on the trespasser, it flared up then narrowed. As silent as a shadow, the leopard leapt down from the tree and trod towards the intruder.

Only instinct warned the enemy. As it turned, it was met with a raking blow by the leopard, followed by a quick bite to the flank. The enemy leopard roared in agony, then pounced on the original. Falling under the heavy blow, the leopard retaliated by landing a heavy kick to the ribs, sending the enemy soaring into the lagoon. The leopard returned to its tree resting its head on its paws as it watched the chaotic scene below.

The rival leopard was dragged into the depths of the pool by a ravenous crocodile. The rival managed one last howl before it disappeared under the surface. The leopard sighed. Peace . . . finally.

Jordan Senior (10)
Crowlees CE(C) J&I School

A DAY IN THE LIFE OF A JAPANESE PRISONER OF WAR

It was treacherous, you could hear the pain going off in the battlerfields. The sound rang out from the bullets being fired, in my imagination as I was a Japanese prisoner of war.

All I ate for five whole years was a portion of rice and a cup of dirty water each day. Maybe some days I went without. I was lucky, very lucky indeed for the Americans saved me. After those five years which seemed like ten I was rescued.

When I returned to the battlefields in Europe, I couldn't believe what I saw, scattered all over the fields were men who fought for my country: England. My mind was flooded with memories of my friends who had died. Even though we had won all those six years we were fighting (1939 - 1945).

We were all bold and had courage, even though we were filled with bad memories. This didn't stop our determination of winning and it didn't because we had won. We had beaten the Germans and there also were streams of blood running down the field. Why did we fight? We fought to save our country and we did save it, but we didn't save men to live on it. We didn't gain men we lost them. What for though? It was all for the sake of a stupid argument that we couldn't agree on, so we fought. Men gave their lives up for England. I have a friend called Leo and he went into the jungle with 200 men and came back with 6. Only 6, and he was one of them.

Sometimes I look back at these memories and I feel that I was very lucky. These memories bring tears, lots of tears. Only I and the other men who gave up their lives in 1939 have had the experience of fighting in the Second World War.

Joanna Barker (10)
Crowlees CE(C) J&I School

A Day In The Life Of A Nurse

I was wandering about and thinking what kind of medicine I should give to my patient and what kind of medicine she would be needing. So I just gave her a letter that said 'Go to the hospital on Friday and have a check up. About your tonsillitis.'

I saw my next patient who was dying of a disease. The disease was called cancer. She had cancer in her leg.

The next day I went straight to the woman who had cancer and I saw that another nurse was giving her blood so that she would live. But the doctor said she only had two months left to live. After a week I asked the doctor if he could give her an operation and the doctor said he could.

The next day he did an operation on the woman to remove the cancer in her leg. He had to take parts out that had caused the disease. The operation took seven hours and after a week or so the woman could not move. She was like a scarecrow. I gave her some tablets to make her feel better but they just did not work. The woman felt quite a bit better but was still depressed. She was feeling quite sad that she might die. But I said to her 'Don't be upset, Nothing's going to happen to you.'

But she really did die and when she died she reminded me of my sister and what had happened to her and how she had died.

After all the sadness I went through with people dying, I left my job.

Sanniya Khan (10)
Crowlees CE(C) J&I School

A DAY IN THE LIFE OF A VET

I am a vet and I help animals that are hurt. When animals are hurt they cannot help themselves, so I help them to get better, but sometimes I just cannot help them, so they have to be put down, so they have a life in Heaven where no one can hurt them. It is sad when they have to be put down, but it takes the pain away. When I save them I am happy because they are not hurt, they are happy and run around. Today I have saved two cats called Patch and Spotty that had stones in their tummies and a dog that had a broken leg. There was a dwarf lop eared rabbit that had been attacked by a Border Collie. The rabbit had its leg bitten off. There was blood everywhere. It had to be put down. I was very sad. I put the rabbit in a box with cotton wool in the bottom, and then I buried it in a shallow hole so it would not go to the devil. I think that being a vet is a great job because if you love animals then you should help them. Then the animals will not be hurt anymore.

Megan Aguirregoicoa (10)
Crowlees CE(C) J&I School

A DAY IN THE LIFE OF ISAAC NEWTON

Hello, I'm Isaac Newton, yes the inventor of the mirror telescope. I've been wondering about how the world is round and how we stay up right wherever we are, even when we are upside down like in Australia. I started wondering about a week ago when an apple fell on my head. How could an apple fall on my head when Britain is on the top side of Earth. So I invited my sister round for breakfast, she is extremely clever. She told me how it was God using his powers, but I still don't understand. I've been doing some research, like dropping balls and measuring how long it takes for it to fall down. But how do birds fly? Maybe I should catch one and find out. But for today I'm tired.

Taheri Behnam (10)
Crowlees CE(C) J&I School

A Day In The Life Of An Archaeologist

'Hey look, I've found a tomb,' he shouted triumphantly.
All the other men came running over to him and started chanting
'Let's explore. Let's explore.'
So they went inside and started to explore. They found out that it was
the tomb of Tutankhamun. When they got into the tomb they found on
the neck of Tutankhamun a bite mark, then somebody screamed and
everybody turned around. They looked around and on the floor then
they saw it was Lord Carnarevon. He was lying on the floor with a bite
mark on his neck. One of the people said
'We better leave him alone otherwise we could die too.'
Then somebody else agreed.

So when they got into the final chamber they saw shining gold jewels
and treasures and pots and toys he used to play with when he was little.
Then they saw the case. It had writing on it so they knew there was a
curse written on his case. When they had taken out some items to study
they went out then they found another tomb on the way back so they
went in that tomb as well it was the tomb of a man who nobody knew.
He also had a curse but luckily they weren't affected by it. They took
some items from the tomb as well.

When they got back they each studied an item and wrote a report, then
just before dawn they put the items back and put the reports in their
files, then after a tiring day of looking and finding items from different
tombs then they went home to their families.

Emma Lockwood (10)
Crowlees CE(C) J&I School

A DAY IN THE LIFE OF A FROG

One important day of life was when I was young and I was told that I could eat things. They told me that I could eat flies and they showed me how to catch them. They told me to put my tongue out as far as I could and catch it but I tried to but I could never do it. Two years later I could eat flies and they showed me how to catch them. They told me to put my tongue out as far as I could and catch it but I tried to, but I could never do it. But two years later I could do it at last. Then they said that you can swim in water when you are older. I was very nervous because my uncle Slime-back drowned in a pond when I was a baby. I was very upset because he was always there for me and he was really polite. I can always remember his last cuddle he gave me and it was a nice big slimy one. I still love him forever even though he's dead. I started to swim and I couldn't because it was cold and deep and I was really nervous because of my Uncle Slime-back. Then I thought 'I won't be scared. I will do it because everybody will laugh at me and tease me loads, and I mean loads.'

My father said 'You can do it son, you can do it.'
So I slid into the water. It was cold, mucky and deep and I felt horrible but I tried. I wasn't going to be teased. I was going to be brave and I did it. I was swimming smoothly along the water and then I went under the water and back up again. I could swim from that day on and I got used to the coldness and the deepness and murkiness and then I was a very very good swimmer.

Jake Crossley (10)
Crowlees CE(C) J&I School

A DAY IN THE LIFE OF A ROMAN

I would get up and go downstairs to the table and have my breakfast. After my breakfast I would go to the baths and talk to my friends. When I had had enough, I went home to get ready for training at the archery range. When I had finished archery training I went home for dinner. I went to the arena to watch a gladiator fight a tiger. The gladiator was very good, he killed the tiger. Then they sent a centurion out. The centurion killed the gladiator, so we went home to have our tea. For tea we had chicken and bread in gravy. When I had finished my tea I got ready for night military training. Night military training goes on all night. Night military training is at the edge of the city. You have to break through a wall, then shoot at the archery target (you have to hit the red or yellow). When you have hit the red or yellow part of the target you have to rescue a prisoner from a wood cell and get out as fast as you can. When everyone is out you have finished, and you can go home. When I got home I went straight to bed.

Graham Kirkby (9)
Crowlees CE(C) J&I School

THE DAY IN THE LIFE OF A PACK OF WOLVES

The pack of wolves began their day by searching for water and then shade. Most of the day they lazed around and did a little bit of hunting. At nightfall it's time to hunt. The pack search for a suitable prey, finally a deer appears. The wolves sneak up from all different angles and *bam!* The wolves pounce, their teeth sink into the deer's neck, their prey falls down dead. The wolves drag their prey to a safe place.

The extremely hungry wolves eat in order, from the oldest wolf to the youngest cub. When the last of the carcass is finished the cubs will nap. After nap time is over it's time to play, which means fighting and practising hunting for when they are fully grown.

Jenny Chester (10)
Crowlees CE(C) J&I School

A DAY IN THE LIFE OF A DOG

A dog is something that barks, that wakes me up in the morning. Every time something or someone goes past it barks. I wonder if they know what I say to them. Do they understand English? When they live in a small house I wonder if they need fresh air. When they go out for a walk they always chase birds and squirrels. Why do they always need to go out and we don't? Dogs go out, they sniff the flowers.

Why do dogs eat dog food? When they go after a cat the cat goes 'miaow.' The dogs go 'woof.' They surge through the streets of London. Their owners shout them to come back. They go back to get some food. They go out for a minute then they go to sleep. The dogs snore.

Danny Broadley (10)
Crowlees CE(C) J&I School

A DAY IN THE LIFE OF MICHAEL OWEN

I woke up in the morning. I knew it was going to be a good day. I was so nervous that I could hardly eat my breakfast. It was 6.30am. I had to be at training for 7.00am. Instead of driving I put on my trainers and ran to the training ground. It was cold and misty. I went into the changing rooms and put on my tracksuit.

The sun was just coming out and we had three hours of training to do. In training we first did some running and then we did some new skills. After that we had a small game. When we had finished all the team went back to the hotel. There were many people waiting for us to sign autographs.

It was coming close to 2.00pm, we had to go to the stadium. All the team were nervous, we could see Arsenal arriving. They all looked nervous as well. It was time for kick-off. Arsenal won the toss, so they kicked off. The match had started. Both teams had a lot of chances, this carried on until half-time. It was nil-nil. It was time for the second half. Liverpool took the kick-off and twenty minutes into it Arsenal scored. After that I scored. It was the last minute and the ball played through to me and I got the winning goal. It was full-time and we went to collect the FA Cup.

Daniel Jones (11)
Crowlees CE(C) J&I School

A Day In The Life Of My Friend Zoe Kemp

7.30am

I woke up early in the morning and turned off my alarm clock. It was Wednesday morning and I had to go to school to do all the work I was told to do.

8.00am

I had my breakfast and got changed and I was watching Kenan and Kel Show with my brother. Antony was talking to his girlfriend on his mobile phone.

8.30am

I was walking to school with all my heavy books and bags ready to start a new day of school work.

9.00am

I was reading a book called Black Beauty while Miss Bright was doing the registers.

9.30am

I have just sung my favourite song in assembly called, 'When I'm Sixty-Four'.

10.00am

My class, 5V were in the middle of literacy hour doing words from other origins and were reading Geordie and Scouser poems, we made our own verse to go with the poems.

10.30am

It was time for me to go and play. I had my Nutragrain bar for my break.

11.00am

This was the best part of the day, maths. I was doing division, my favourite.

11.30

Miss went through the answers of the homework because she forgot to do them yesterday.

1.30am
I came back from dinner and Miss was doing the register again.

2.00am
Miss Bright told us to do our Tudor work. It was time for me to go.

Stephanie Clayton (9)
Crowlees CE(C) J&I School

A DAY IN THE LIFE OF A VET

Every morning I open the pure white doors to the vets and take the short walk to my office. I say, 'Hi,' to Spunky, my favourite spaniel, then I feed the rabbits, guinea pigs and the rats. Usually I sit in my office for an hour sorting papers, then my first patient comes in.

My first patient is a lady with a cat. She seemed very upset but the cat only had a slight stomach-ache but it was miaowing very loudly and it wouldn't eat. So I guess she did have the right to be upset. I gave her some pills and said really poshly, 'Just take her home and give her one pill a day.' She seemed a lot better when she had realised what was wrong. Then when she opened the door I nearly fainted. There was a huge line, all waiting for me.

The first person in the line looked like he had run a mile. His face was pale, his hair was messy and he looked really shocked and he said with a few words, 'Animals dying at farm.' That was when I knew there was trouble for sure. He grabbed my hand and ran, he threw me in a car and drove off at seventy miles an hour. He stopped at a farm and he ran into a sheep field and took me to a big fat sheep. It was laying on the ground and I gazed at it, it looked fine really but I still gave it a check-up. Then I realised it had foot and mouth disease. That made my heart sink.

Really quickly I had to phone some more vets to check out the rest of the herd, then I thought the only way to prevent the disease was to kill the herd, but I couldn't do that to the animals. I love them but I realised it was the only way. Anyway, it was already in the farmer's head. They were due to be killed the next day. I didn't go to sleep that night, I just kept thinking of the herd. Then I realised I didn't have to kill them, I could call the army. So straight away the next morning I phoned up the army. No one was there but I gave them a message. It was horrible waiting but then finally I got a call, I wasn't off the hook so sadly I got my boots and went to the farm.

Then I pulled back the trigger and before you knew it I had shot all the herd. That night I was really pleased I had shot the herd because they were going to die painfully otherwise. So I guess it was best to get it over with.

Kate Ramsden (10)
Crowlees CE(C) J&I School

A Day In The Life Of Whitney Houston

I was stood looking at all the pop stars and just thinking I was one. I never thought I would end up driving a limousine and getting out and seeing all my fans. I said, 'Is it my looks or my voice?'
A girl aged ten came to me and said, 'It is both Whitney, both.'

I was really, really pleased with what she said and it helped me in my concert. I could see the little girl in the back now jumping and singing. The day went fast and I still needed to do a lot of work. I finished my concert with a song everybody loves. It was quite slow but still the best of all time.

Kimberley Delaney (10)
Crowlees CE(C) J&I School

A DAY IN THE LIFE OF CHARLOTTE LAVERICK

Today my day was really fun, we played games. I played with Laura, Brooke, Alice, Lucy and Rebecca and many more. We had loads of fun.

We were doing SATs all morning, they were quite hard but I think I did all right. Laura and I both finished, but we were really nervous at first.

In dinner we sat on a table together. We all made fun of Laura's laugh, it's really funny. After dinner we played wall tig again. Laura was on.

When we came in after play Laura sat next to me as we were doing quiet reading. I like sitting next to Laura. We were discussing the White Rose Centre, we both couldn't wait until Saturday.

In class we did science, art, map work and PE. We played cricket, I ran as fast as I could but I was caught out in the end and only Laura was left, we were all out apart from her. She ran and she wasn't out but when she ran for a second time she was caught out, we were all exhausted.

My day was really fun and I love being with my friends, they are so much fun. I can't wait until tomorrow to be with them again, they make the school a happy place to be. I really feel happy when they are around, they liven up my life and make me feel special.

Laura Brocklebank (10)
Crowlees CE(C) J&I School

A Day In The Life Of My Dad

I woke up to my daily work and ate my breakfast. My wife had made it for me. After that I got changed for my work, I do plumbing. My wife took me to work, just like any other wife does for her husband. About twenty-five minutes later I arrived at work. That day I was going to help an old lady to do her sink, because the flow pipe had burst, I insisted on helping her. She seemed to be able to only slightly move, but when she wanted to help she became a bit faster. It was harder than I thought and the lady didn't seem to mind. We had to go get some supplies or the pipe would surely flood. She took me in her car and hurried there so we didn't waste any time. Finally we got there.

'You go and get it while I park,' she said slowly.

'OK!'

I hurried and bought it, not knowing what had happened to the pipe, whether it had flooded, or whether the old lady had no sink. We dashed to the lady's house to find the sink as it always was, we then fixed the pipe in its place. She thanked me and I went back home on the bus. The old lady seemed different from when I first met her. I got home and said hi to my child. He said hi to me, but in a peculiar way. I ate my tea and read the paper. I was reading an advert about football. Then, I went to sleep in my cosy warm bed, waiting for a new day.

Ben Brownhill (10)
Crowlees CE(C) J&I School

A DAY IN THE LIFE OF TIGER WOODS

Today was a very good day because I won The Open.

The day had started off as a miserable day, it was the fourth day of The Open. I prepared for the day and had breakfast.

We got out at one o'clock and played until four o'clock but it was a tie between me and Lee Westwood, so we played sudden death on the first hole. The first hole is a par three and one hundred and twenty-eight yards to the pin.

We were on the first green and I putted my birdie shot. Lee Westwood putted his birdie shot. So the second hole is now sudden death.

The second hole is par four and five hundred and seventy-two yards to the pin.

We were on the green when a duck picked my ball up and swam in the lake with it in its mouth. So I placed another ball down and putted for par. Lee Westwood had a long birdie putt and he missed. So it was third hole sudden death.

The third hole is a par four and five hundred and sixty-one yards.

I was on the fairway, it had been a bad hole. Luckily my third shot was on the green. Lee Westwood had a chance for a birdie to win. The putt flew by the hole. I putted and got par. Lee had a try to stay in the game and missed. I won The Open and I celebrated all night.

The day has been excellent.

Thomas Stratford (11)
Crowlees CE(C) J&I School

A DAY IN THE LIFE OF ROLF HARRIS

When I was on my holiday in Australia I stumbled upon an injured kangaroo on a walk. Immediately I ran for help. I flew into the hotel remembering just down the corridor was a vet. I knocked constantly until he stirred. I told him what had happened, he got changed and came with me. It was obvious to us that it was serious.

I drove while the vet cared for the kangaroo in the back. When we arrived there the diagnosis was that it had been shot with an air rifle in the upper part of its leg. It had shattered the thigh bone. It would take years to heal, so it was decided to amputate its leg. I was devastated and broke down in tears.

The operation went well and after the anaesthetic had worn off he staggered around. Because I had found him I had the privilege of naming him. I called him Wonky (due to his wonky jumps). The vet told me he would not be able to be released into the wild.

Every time I visit Australia now I always go to visit Wonky. He lives with another twenty kangaroos in a one acre enclosure. We will be friends forever.

James Rotchell (11)
Crowlees CE(C) J&I School

A Day In The Life Of Jennifer Lopez

I can't wait, in thirty minutes I'm going on stage. I'm so excited hearing my fans scream and shout, it is great. When the judge shouts, 'Jennifer Lopez,' it will be exciting. In a way though I'm scared, what if they don't like me or my songs? It won't be like that though anyway (well I hope).

I get to wear cool clothes and learn ace dance moves. I'm on, 'Here comes Jennifer Lopez with her new single, 'Play'.' Listen to all my fans screaming and chanting. first I'm singing 'Play', here goes . . .

Yes! My fans love it I've got to get changed for my next song. I'm wearing a little skirt and hot pants. 'Now Jennifer Lopez will sing 'Love Don't Cost A Thing'.' Yes I think they really like it, there's a break now. When I start singing all my fans cheer, scream, chant. I love being a pop star but sometimes it's hard work and tiring as well.

I'm back on now and it's my last song for this concert. I'm singing 'Waiting For Tonight'.

'This is Jennifer's last song so let's scream, chant and shout before she goes.'

I really enjoy being a pop star and I hope for the future I can do more concerts and be even more popular with my fans.

Brooke Oliver (11)
Crowlees CE(C) J&I School

A DAY IN THE LIFE OF SUZANNE FROM HEAR'SAY

I woke up this morning and opened the mail to find out I was in the band, Hear'say. I was over the moon. I was so happy I wanted to run outside and tell the whole world. One problem, I was still in my pyjamas. I read on to find I'd to be in the studio in two hours.

When I arrived at the studios I felt afraid and scared, I didn't know what to expect. When I went in I saw three other members, Myleene, Danny and Noel - so who were we waiting for? The doors opened and Kym walked in; so I guessed they were my fellow pop stars. I turned round to see Nasty Nigel, Paul our composer and a choreographer. First, Nigel talked to us about the band and things like that. Then Paul told us about our new song, 'Pure and Simple' and he showed us the words.

So today we're learning our song, we all did that until 1.30pm. As a treat we all had McDonald's for lunch. We came back and recorded our song and then I just had this feeling it would be a hit!

As I went home I felt so happy I could have cried. When I got home I did, I was overwhelmed with emotion. So I rung everyone I knew to tell them the news.

Lois Rowling (11)
Crowlees CE(C) J&I School

A DAY IN THE LIFE OF RACHEL FROM S CLUB 7

What, he must be joking! How can I get lots of sleep in half an hour? It's already two and he wants me here again for half past! He's mad! We are humans you know.

'Brrr!'
'What, I got no sleep,' moaned Hannah.
'I don't think anyone did,' I said.
'Wow! You three look washed out!' I commented as the boys walked in.
'Come on, let's go!' exclaimed Jo waking up.

When we arrived there I knew we were up for another hard day, but, it's worth it, seeing everyone so happy, I'm glad I am able to put a smile on people's faces.

We went through the whole thing again. I try to be good and then we can have some dinner, but we didn't get anything until 4pm, then the show starts. People either love or hate you but as long as our fans and S Club 7 are happy so am I.

Yes we've finished. When we were about to go . . . Wow! A fan had waited two hours to see me! I went up to her and said, 'Do you want my autograph?'
She nodded her head with a big smile on her face.
'What's your name?' I asked.
'Jade,' she whispered.
'To Jade,' I wrote, 'Lots of love,' I carried on, and put my autograph. She gave me something and ran off.
'Thank you!' I shouted after her.

We drove off. Then . . .
'Brrrr!' went my clock.
Another day!

Rachel Wise (11)
Crowlees CE(C) J&I School

A Day In The Life Of Jean Claude Van Damme

Today I went down to the gym to practise my kick-boxing. When I got there, there was Arnold Schwarzenegger asking me to team up with him for Predator 3 and Terminator 2. I couldn't resist so I said, 'Yes.' Then the next minute I was practising my kick-boxing for the two moves that I had to film tomorrow. After I had finished I was going to the Oscars and I got three awards. One for best male, the 2nd for best actor and the third for best actor in the world. Arnold won two awards, I was pleased for the man so I shook his hand and we made the headlines.

For dinner I went to the pizza shop and bought a ham and cheese pizza. Then the next minute I was swept off my feet leaving my pizza behind and I was rushed to the hospital where my mother was. The doctor told me that her house was on fire and they just got her out in time, she only suffered cuts and burns.

At 3.40 I was surrounded by fans asking me for my autograph. By the end of the day I was like a sitting duck just waiting till the pain went away.

At night there was nothing on television so I went to bed.

Sam Taylor (11)
Crowlees CE(C) J&I School

A DAY IN THE LIFE OF KYLIE MINOGUE

It's my big day today because I've got my big concert tonight at Manchester Arena. I'm really nervous because I've never done a concert before and it will be the first time my fans get the chance to come and see me. They also get to hear songs that have never been released as well so that'll be great too. The other good thing is that fans who don't see me in concert can buy a video of my performance in the shops from the 3rd of June 2001.

It's 11.00am and it's time for my first rehearsal of the day. I'm getting nervous even though it's not the real thing. Right I'm on.
'I'm spinning around, move out of my way, I know I'm feeling like this 'cause you like it like this.'
Oops the sound track wasn't right so I'll have to wait until they get it right. Doing the concert I think is going to help me be less nervous for when I perform on other shows like 'Top of the Pops', 'Pepsi Chart Show', 'Brits' and loads more because I think once I've performed tonight I'll be able to perform anywhere, on any TV programme and with any song too, which will be great.

Now it's 5.30pm, it's been great fun rehearsing but I feel as though I've been locked up in a cage for a million years because all I've been doing is rehearsing. In a minute I have to go to the sandwich bar to get some tea so I'll see you at the concert.

Bye for now!

Jessica Blackburn (10)
Crowlees CE(C) J&I School

A DAY IN THE LIFE OF MARK VIDUKA

Today is the best day of my career because when we played Chelsea I scored a scorching goal, it was a good match against them but I had loads of opportunities to score.

Alan Smith set me up with the goal because he just hit it over the top of everybody and I just hit it and it went in.

Robbie Keane then came on for Alan Smith and he scored but there was only two minutes remaining in the second-half.

I am enjoying myself playing for Leeds United and David O'Leary is an excellent coach, he helps us through things when we lose.

I am pretty good at scoring with my head. I think I have got a bit of a skill but I'm not as good as Alan Smith.

I think my worst match was against Valencia because I never got stuck in, I wasn't doing much work, I was just leaving it all to Alan Smith.

I think I done well in the Premiership because I have scored lots of goals for my team. I have also set a couple of goals up especially when we played Charlton because I did a back heel to Alan Smith and he just put it straight into the back of the net. If anybody tried to buy me I would not go. I will stay with Leeds United.

Anthony Senior (11)
Crowlees CE(C) J&I School

A DAY IN THE LIFE OF THE WRESTLER, UNDERTAKER

Today was unlike any other day. It was the day I became WWF Champion. I went down to the arena to help Kane with defeating Triple H. I gave him tips on using the chain to his advantage like choking Triple H with the chain. Kane was ready for Triple H and I was confident Kane would win.

In Kane's match at Judgement Day everything was going fine until Stone Cold went down to the ring and hit Kane with a steel chair. Suddenly Kane's fate was in my hands. I rushed down to the ring and started beating up Triple H and Stone Cold. I gave Triple H his last ride and finally choke slammed Stone Cold. 1, 2, 3, Kane had pinned and won the Intercontinental Championship.

Now it was my match, my judgement day. My entrance music sounded and everybody gave me a standing ovation and cheered for me. The whole arena was intense. The match started and I hammered Stone Cold with a numerous amount of upper cuts. I felt great, I was about to win the title but then . . . Vince came down to the ring but to my surprise Stone Cold hit him with a chair. I did the 'Last Ride' on Stone Cold and pinned him for a three count. I couldn't believe that I regained the title and once again I was the best. When the referee raised my hand in victory with the title I was very satisfied.

William Best (11)
Crowlees CE(C) J&I School

A Day In The Life Of Katie Philpot

I went shopping this morning, it was brilliant. I bought some new clothes and some new dancing shoes. I went with my best friend and we had a great time. We bought some new strawberry ice cream and it was really nice.

We didn't get any lunch so I got a prawn and salad sandwich, from Maun's on the way to the gym. When I got there I went to the aerobics class. I went on an exercise bike and lifted some weights. I also enjoyed the aqua aerobics and it made me feel good and it soothed my bones.

After that I went home tired out and then I felt really bad because the dancing outfits arrived, so I had to sort those out.

Next I went to the Zion Baptist Church for my dancing lessons. The first lesson I taught was ballet, then jazz, then it was the older jazz class. By this time I was worn out but I kept going. Finally another day had gone.

It was brilliant though, I mean so what if I was moaning through all the day, I still enjoyed it. After all it does keep you in shape.

Lucy McDermott (10)
Crowlees CE(C) J&I School

A Day In The Life Of Michael Owen

My name is Michael Owen, I am twenty-one years old and I play football for Liverpool FC. On the back of my shirt is the number ten. I get up in the morning thinking who will I be playing next and will I save the day by getting the golden goal? My team-mates and I have just won three cups. We finished third in the league. I go training four or five times a week, usually we do press-ups, star jumps, running around the track or having a little game of football.

I have just bought my family a new house. I have a dog to play with when I am not training. Today, I am going out with my mum and dad for dinner. I go on lots of TV programmes such as 'Live and Kicking', to have a chat. Everyone wants my autograph. In the future I hope that I will maintain my good form and continue to score lots of goals and be part of a successful Liverpool team.

Stephanie Harrison (10)
Crowlees CE(C) J&I School

A DAY IN THE LIFE OF RACHEL FROM S CLUB 7

I woke up this morning feeling nervous and happy at the same time. I felt nervous because we were doing a concert at 7.30pm and happy because the concerts would all be over tomorrow. Yippee!

As I arrived at Sheffield Arena at approximately 5.00pm I felt more nervous than ever. You'll think I'm silly because you will think I've done one before but it's my first time. Bradley and Jo are calm about it and the others (Tina, Jon, Paul and Hannah) only sing a bit.

When there was only ten minutes to go until the concert started I could hear all the screams coming from fans and I was so glad because I didn't think there would be so many people out there.

The good thing was that when I got into it I was fine and after the show I couldn't wait for the next day!

After the show a girl who had won a competition on the radio, came back stage to meet us and I told her all about the story and she just laughed!

It was about 2.00am when we were all in bed chatting. I was in the middle of my sentence when I just fell asleep.

Stefani Fox (11)
Crowlees CE(C) J&I School

A Day In The Life Of My Dad

When I woke up this morning, I suddenly remembered my wedding day where my son, Tom, was the best man. This was my second wedding. At the church Tom handed the vicar the rings perfectly, because in my eyes he is perfect. Later on at the reception Tom did his speech and I thought it was excellent. Then came the moment of truth, it was time for me to do my speech, Tom knew it was time because I was crying.

I think one of the things my son admires about me is my strength because once when I took him to work with me he couldn't lift any of the barrels but I could. I also think he admires the way I listen to him.

I then got up and went downstairs and had my breakfast, said goodbye to Tom when he went to school. At twelve o'clock I went to Pontefract where I work at Asda as a lorry drive. I came home at nine o'clock, said goodnight to Tom and relaxed with my wife. At about half past ten I read and went to sleep before I wake up ready for the next day.

Thomas Moggridge (11)
Crowlees CE(C) J&I School

A Day In The Life Of Sandro Westerveld

My day starts with me falling out of bed, then putting on some clothes. I then slowly walk downstairs and have three Weetabix. Once I had finished I started to play football and the ball hit my mum's favourite vase. Oops!

I headed for the door too worried to do anything else. I got into my car (putting my kit in the boot). When I got to the stadium I saw the squad waiting for me. I was ten minutes late!

Gary McAllister told me to go and shave, so I went to the changing room and did so. Training had already started, I quickly put my kit on and ran to the goal. Gerrard Houllier wasn't pleased at all. It was the reserve team against the normal team. I was playing on the normal team.

Two minutes into the practise match it was 2-1 to us. I let in a really embarrassing goal where Zeige toe-poked the ball, it rolled in.

It was time for lunch, I was eating my crisps in a quiet corner thinking how to impress Houllier.

The next ten minutes were dull, nobody seemed to get near the box. Finally my time came, Babbel had fouled Zeige in the box!

'Come on!' Owen shouted, 'Save it!' I did just that, I dived to the left and saved it.

The rest of the game was more exciting, four more goals were scored and I saved nine great kicks. I went home feeling very relieved.

Matthew Chandler (11)
Crowlees CE(C) J&I School

A DAY IN THE LIFE OF THOMAS I

Hello, I am Thomas and I'll tell you about myself. I'm not scared of anything, people call me smart but I don't think I am. I have two horrible sisters called Amy and Billy. I always finish what I start and I have two cats and a very kind mum. I have lots of friends and I go home to a peaceful house every day. I have quite a small bedroom which is one of eight rooms in my house. I complete my homework and put all problems right.

I was born in Dewsbury hospital and I'm ten years old. I live in a big field that I play in with my sister Amy. I like technical things. My birthday is the 18th of June. In the morning (8.30am) I walk to school and I play tig before I go in. We start work at 9.35am after assembly. I have maths first and after break I have English. Maths and English go on for one hour. After English we have dinner break. Sometimes we are allowed on the field when I jump around and play football. Then after that we have topic work for three hours and thirty minutes and then I go home. The best bit of the day!

Daniel Wright (11)
Crowlees CE(C) J&I School

A DAY IN THE LIFE OF MICHAEL OWEN

My day begins when I get out of my four-poster bed, which is covered in curry boxes, cos my favourite food is curry. I'm not a very healthy eater but I make up for it in the gym.

Anyway I'm shaving with my pink fluffy razor. Now I'm putting my Y-fronts on, now my best Liverpool kit that my mum washed herself. Then I started playing football with a piece of paper. I broke my mum's favourite ornament, then I ran. I jumped in the car (which is a Ford GT90). I set off to Anfield for training. I was ten minutes late. Gerrard Houllier was in a good mood so he let me off.

We had a penalty shot. The score was 5-5 and if I scored we would win. I scored it, then I went to Houllier's house hoping to get a pay rise. I didn't get it though, because he was still sober. Anyway I had a great time. He makes a great chilli and a mean hot chocolate fudge cake, but the best bit was the home-made ice cream. Sandro called over after tea. We had a couple of cans. I drove home, I went through a red light and crashed into a Ford Focus. I put a hundred pounds under the windscreen.

When I got home I feel asleep in the dog's kennel.

Ben Renshaw (11)
Crowlees CE(C) J&I School

A DAY IN THE LIFE OF ALAN SHEARER

Hi I am Alan Shearer and I was born in the year 1970 in Newcastle.

Today I met my old friends, and Kevin Keegan and I had a game of football with them.

After we travelled in my car over 700 miles to get to America. Half way to America my mobile started ringing - it was the England manager who asked me if I could play against America and I said yes.

When we got there the England manager gave me my old shirt, the number nine shirt and the captain's armband.

All my friends were there like Owen and Seaman. It was just like the Charity Shield Final that I played with Newcastle.

The referee blew the whistle and ten minutes into the first half I scored a header. The rest of the game was boring - no one scored. The final whistle went and I had scored the winner with my old team.

That night me and the lads went to the pub and had a pint of lager.

On the way home I had another phone call from the England manager, he asked me if I wanted a career with England. I said I did and I was the England Number Nine again.

On the way home my wife called me and asked me how my day went. She was amazed that I had another career with England as I had retired only one month ago.

All this made me tired and I fell fast asleep.

Ross Taylor (11)
Crowlees CE(C) J&I School

143

A DAY IN THE LIFE OF DAVID BECKHAM

I am David Beckham and I am a football player. I play for Man United and on my shirt I wear the number seven with my surname Beckham.

When I was playing against Argentina with my team in the World Cup I got sent off. Also I am the captain of England after Alan Shearer retired as the captain.

I am married to a pop star called Victoria who comes from the Spice Girls. Victoria and I got married and had a baby. The baby is a boy and we named him Brooklyn.

When I wake up in the morning, I always think about playing football and who we will play next.

In the week when I have all my days off me, Victoria and Brooklyn go out shopping and go to parks but when we don't do that I go training which takes place in Manchester. When I am there I sometimes see Paul Scholes.

When I go out to places I am always ready to give out my autograph because there are always people who recognise me.

When it comes to having days off the most I have is about three and the least is one day, so it doesn't really give me much time to see my family, but when I have the chance I take my family out for dinner.

Rebecca Sheard (11)
Crowlees CE(C) J&I School

A DAY IN THE LIFE OF MY AUNTIE GILL

My Auntie Gill on Sundays can sometimes be very busy but on Sunday 20th May she was especially busy. This is how I think her day went.

I got woken up by Alex Stratford. I had a little breakfast, normally a slice of toast maybe two. Then I got washed and put on my red round-necked shirt, my blue jodphurs, my black boots and my black hat. I picked up Alex. She jumped in the passenger seat and off we went to the stables. On the way we talked about school and how things went with our SATs.

Alex said, 'I'm glad SATs are over!'

When we got to the stables I got on Trevor and Alex got on Frank. We started our lesson at 11.00 am. Alex had been taking horse-riding lessons longer than me so she was having an hour's lesson and I had half an hour's lesson.

I started off walking and changing the rein from A to C, then trotting, I wasn't quite ready for cantering. They taught me how to remember the order of the letters of the arena but I can't remember it.

Alex and I got home and had a jacket potato with beans. After that I had to leave Alex because she had to clean her rabbit out.

I went to see Leeds play Valencia. I drove there with my brother. Sadly they lost 4-2 but they played very well. Then I went to the pub and stayed for an hour. Then I went home and fed the dog and went to bed.

Alexandra Stratford (11)
Crowlees CE(C) J&I School

A DAY IN THE LIFE OF MY MUM

When I get up, I get washed and dressed and go downstairs to have my breakfast. I then send the children off to school and I go to work at a quarter to nine.

I work with children from the age of 4-6. It sometimes gets very messy.

I work until 3.00 pm but then I have to tidy up till quarter past then get home in time for the children. I then get changed into casual clothes and then tidy up. I then sit down with a cup of tea to watch TV. I get their tea ready and after that I help them with their homework.

Then I get their dad's tea ready and wait for him to come home. Then I either go on the computer or write a letter or do a crossword. Then I send my children off to bed. I go to bed at a later time but before that I get my clothes ready for the morning.

Caroline Ramsden (10)
Crowlees CE(C) J&I School

A Day In The Life Of David Beckham

I love being a professional football player, especially for Manchester United.

The beginning of my day is always different, but the best one is when there is a football match in the morning at Old Trafford. I wake up at 6.15, get my breakfast and after that I tell Victoria I am going. I then set off to Old Trafford in my Ferrari.

I go through the main entrance where I have to show my ID card to the receptionist. After that I go into the changing room where I see Alex, also Ryan, Phil and Gary. They're nearly always the first ones there, the last one there is Roy Keane, I don't know why though.

Before Alex says anything at all we wait for everyone to be there. He tells us our formation and our positions and about half an hour before the match we warm up and have a kick around.

When we exit the tunnel on to the pitch, the crowd is ecstatic.

After the match we enter the showers and clean off all the mud on our legs. Alex either congratulates us on our win or gives us a rollicking if we lose and play absolutely rubbish.

I then go back to my wife and I then have about an hour's sleep.

Chris Crossley (11)
Crowlees CE(C) J&I School

A Day In The Life Of Britney Spears

It's been really hard today because I've just recorded my new song 'Stronger', plus I was late to start because my alarm didn't go off. It's quite hard being a famous singer and dancer.

I must say its brilliant being famous but I miss all of my friends and my family a lot. The best thing is being able to sing in front of people.

I've got a concert coming up soon, well next week and when the tickets went out on sale they all sold within two hours.

In my life the thing that spoils my day is not being a normal person. I really wish I could have more time with my family and friends. I can't even go out on the streets on my own because of all the people that come up to me.

Sometimes I feel as if I'm caged up in a box and never allowed out. If I could change my life, I would give myself more freedom.

When I first became a pop star I had to lose weight before I went on stage. The best thing that has happened to me is that my first song went to number one.

Sarah Hofstetter (11)
Crowlees CE(C) J&I School

A Day In The Life Of A Cat

I was walking on a wall when suddenly a mouse sprung across the newly-laid tarmac. I leapt down to the floor and I ran to the mouse. It just managed to get in a hole in the tarmac. I swiped at the little mouse and knocked it into the wall. It seemed to look at me in a *'don't eat me'* sort of way. I opened my mouth and attacked the rodent. Crack! The body fell to the ground. I leapt up on to a tree and ate the mouse.

My friend Ginger came and joined me. I dived on to the wall and jumped into the cat flap and out of the back cat flap and into the back garden and on to the shed and over the six foot fence and on to the porch and on to the floor.

As I strolled down the path I saw a thing on two legs and holding a stick with hair on its paws. I quickly jumped out of its way. I listened to its sound then I leapt on to the thing with the stick in its paws and pulled two hairs out of its head. I then ran to the house door and went in and fell asleep.

Ryan Sutcliffe (10)
Crowlees CE(C) J&I School

A Day In The Life Of A Horse

I was ten when it happened. My dad was a scientist who had just invented something that could turn people into horses but those horses would switch bodies with the humans, so here's what happened all those years ago . . .

Dean (my big brother) and I were playing hide and seek tig, when I hid in Dad's laboratory. When Dean saw me I ran into the potion, which fell on me so I shut my eyes. I was a horse! At least I was a nice black one. My new name was Twilight. Then out came a girl, her name was Becky and she was my owner. She tacked me, mounted me then walked me into the field and trotted and cantered me. Then she wanted me to jump. I simply refused so she gave me the whip, oh how it hurt! I backed up and galloped to the other side of the field. I was sold to a farmer who had another horse named Jester.

He was a good fellow, well trained and put all his effort into his work for he was ever so jolly and so he was my new neighbour.

At my other side there was a beautiful lady horse named Melanie. She was obviously the farmer's daughter's horse for she had a purple saddle, reins and everything. She even had a pink fake rose fastened in her hairy mane. Jester and Melanie were obviously in deep, deep love.

Just then the farmer came in and took us all out to the field where he rode me into the square where you do letters so we did that for a while but instead of asking and giving a squeeze of the legs each time, he whacked me with the whip!

Oh how it hurt, being whipped again and again but after the jumps I went to the stables to rest. A car pulled up, it was my dad's. He parked then talked to the farmer, paid a wad of money and took all of us to my human house.

Even if I was still a horse, I was with my family and friends and have made good friends with Melanie and Jester but after that day I was me again!

Georgina Rhodes (9)
Crowlees CE(C) J&I School

A Day In The Life Of James Rotchell

'Wake up you lazy bones, James,' said my mum at 8.15 am. So I woke up and I didn't have any breakfast because I wasn't hungry. I then set off for school.

When I got there all my friends were there and we had to go into class and sit down for ten minutes and then we went to assembly for thirty minutes.

After that we came out of assembly and into an English lesson. Mrs Bell, our teacher, was talking to the class and I started to talk to my friend Peter and then I got told off. Mrs Bell looked at me and stopped talking and said, 'Have you quite finished?'
I said, 'Yes.'

After that Mrs Bell told me to go and sit outside the classroom and do my work out there. At the end of English I came back in the classroom and then it was playtime.

We came back in and we did some maths and I started talking to Peter again and telling Joe to be quiet and that's when I got told off again, but this time I didn't have to go outside. I just had to move to another table with nobody else on it.

After maths it was just a normal day as usual then it was home time, but there was another day to go.

Peter Lockwood (11)
Crowlees CE(C) J&I School

A DAY IN THE LIFE OF ME

I woke up and suddenly I knew it would be the worst day of my life. I had a feeling it would be. I got out of bed and looked at my clock, it was late so I got dressed and ran downstairs and had my breakfast which was a bowl of Weetabix. I then got my coat and packed my bag, I gave Mum a kiss and then ran off to school.

I ran into class and my teacher Mrs Barnto told me off for being late. I sat down and didn't do any work until break. At break I kicked the ball and it missed the goal and it went smash, right through the head teacher's window. She came out and told me to go into her office. I got in and she gave me a big telling off and gave me detention.

After break I got inside and halfway through the lesson I got ink all over the teacher. At dinner I spilled the dinner over one of the dinner ladies. About ten minutes before the end of school, the school caught fire and everybody panicked and ran outside but one boy tripped over a chair. The teacher who checked the register didn't get an answer when she read mine and the boy's name out. She got worried but then she saw me carrying the boy out of the building and she clapped and cheered. The fire brigade came and put out the fire and then it was home time.

I got home and told my mum about everything and she said she would get a treat for me. I said to myself, 'I thought it would be the worst day of my life but actually it was the best day of my life.' I then went to sleep.

Ashley Simpson (11)
Escrick CE Primary School

A Day In The Life Of Roger

'Oh no,' groaned Roger sleepily as he got out of bed. 'Another day at school and I'm already late!' He got his clothes on and went downstairs. He got the cereal out of the cupboard and made his breakfast. He scoffed it quickly, just having time to say goodbye to Mum before going to the bus stop to catch the school bus.

On the bus it was torture, people were throwing paper aeroplanes and bits of rubbish around, shouting as they rode along. The bus stopped at the school gate and the children clambered off. As Roger went into the form room, the teacher asked for homework. He reached into his bag but no homework was in it.

'Where's your homework, Roger?' asked the teacher.
'I don't know,' said Roger.
'Well it's an after-school detention for you,' said the teacher sharply.

The rest of the lesson went well and at the end Roger went to lunch but his pack up was not in his bag. 'Oh no!' exclaimed Roger. 'What will I do now?' So he sold a pen and got a cheap sausage roll.

He went to the lockers to get his PE kit and on the floor was a time bomb, 'Uh-oh!' said Roger and he started smashing it to bits. He ran to the head teacher and gave it to him. He got five pounds and no detention.

Jonathan Bramley (10)
Escrick CE Primary School

A DAY IN THE LIFE OF ME

I opened my eyes. It was a bright, sunny day and I couldn't wait to go outside. It would just be a normal day at school. School was OK but of course the best bit was going home as far as I was concerned.

An hour later, after having breakfast, I was walking to school. I walked round the corner and through the gate and walked into a litter bin.
'Ouch!' I cried. I started rubbing my legs.

Just then my friends came out.
'That was a bit silly,' they said.

I walked away from them and put my bag in the cloakroom. The bell rang and I ran into the classroom.
'Hey, you boy!' the teacher said.
I turned around.
'You're five minutes late, five lines!'

After I'd done my lines, later in the lesson, I got a detention for supposedly talking while the teacher was.

I was in a bad mood at lunchtime and it wasn't improved by me getting told off for not doing chairs, (it wasn't even our week!).

When I came into the classroom after lunch, I thought things couldn't get any worse. I was proven right. In geography I got three team points and in art we were painting pictures.

As I said goodbye to my friends and walked out of the school gate. I thought that life was very strange indeed.

Colin Bramley (10)
Escrick CE Primary School

A DAY IN THE LIFE OF KATE CARTWRIGHT

Where was I? Who was I? Why was I here?

I looked in the mirror and I had just realised I had woken up as Kate Cartwright and it was Monday morning, *'school!'* Kate was the worst girl in the school for good tricks.

I rushed breakfast and getting dressed and hurried along the streets to school but slowly walked across the playground just like Kate, to make everything seem normal.

Just before we went out to play, Mrs Mackie announced that we all had to bring something in tomorrow to show the rest of the class.

The next morning Chris showed his teddy with only one eye, Claire showed her poster of a tabby cat and the morning went rather fast until it was Kate's turn. She went to the front of the room and held out a pale grey stone in her cup-shaped hands. There was a stunned silence.

'Well,' said Mrs Mackie, 'that was very interesting!'
'Not really,' whispered Chris.

Mrs Mackie said that she would like a word with me before the end of school.

I went to Mrs Mackie at the end of school, she said that I had to bring something else in tomorrow, that maybe the class would find a little more exciting.

That night, Kate went and put the stone back in the garden, now that she knew nobody liked it.

Next day . . . It was my turn, and I had nothing else to do except go to the front and show what she had brought in. I went to the front of the classroom and pulled out a small matchbox. Suddenly I dropped the matchbox and . . .

'There it goes!' I shouted, 'It's ginger.'
'Ahh!' shouted Claire while trying to climb on her desk.
Tim quickly jumped on his desk and shouted, 'It's up the curtain!'
'I caught it,' announced Jason.

It was such a shame that Kate didn't see it.

Emily Anderson (10)
Escrick CE Primary School

A DAY IN THE LIFE OF ME

Smack! Just hit the floor. I got up looked at the clock, oh no it's 8.30. I grabbed my clothes, rived them on and ran downstairs at top speed. I grabbed a slice of toast, yanked my bag off the floor and went to school.

I've just finished school and I'm going to the disco. It isn't that far. We're finally there, yahoo I thought. As I went in there it happened, there were no kids there. There were only grown-ups but their music was OK. I didn't dare dance. At least there were some crisps, I picked them up and went outside.

Wow! This is excellent, there's a park, it's humongous. There's a big slide and swing, a climbing frame and everything you could think of.

Time to go and get in the car. A few minutes later and it's good to be at home again. I won't leave home again.

Alex Penistone (10)
Escrick CE Primary School

A DAY IN THE LIFE OF A CHOLERA GERM

I was picked up by the boy when he drank dirty water from a stream. I floated in his gaping mouth, that was when I knew I was inside and deadly. As I rushed down his throat, I laughed inwardly.

I landed with a splash in the boy's stomach juice; I immediately began to enjoy myself. As you may know, we cholera germs revel in heat and moisture. I began to disperse more germs but I was interrupted by those pesky white blood cells. I just touched them and they shrivelled up and died. I smiled and began to multiply again. Ten minutes later there were thousands of us, we began to infect the boy. The inside of the stomach turned pale green as we did our work. I wonder how the boy was feeling. Cold? Scared? In pain? Yes, definitely in pain.

Wait, yes we have done it. We've got to the bloodstream. I floated in and began the wild bloodstream journey. As I shot through the boy's veins I could hear his heart beating. I shot out some disease and everything shook. The heart stopped beating. We had accomplished our mission.

It didn't take long; the boy died in twenty four hours all because he drank dirty water without thinking. If one little thing was different - the boy drinking somewhere else, me staying in some other lake or stream or the boy thinking before he drank - he might still be around today. Me, I wasn't bothered about it. I just put another name on the 'now served' board.

Sam Anderson (11)
Escrick CE Primary School

A DAY IN THE LIFE OF ME

I woke up that morning feeling like nothing on Earth. The sun was shining and I got dressed and went downstairs to eat my breakfast. By eleven o'clock I made a picnic, got on my bike and went to call Rob.

Rob was allowed to come out and we went on the bikes to the common. It was a hot morning with just a light breeze. After an hour or so we sat under an oak tree and ate our picnic. We had cheese and ham sandwiches, scotch eggs, sausage rolls and chocolate muffins. We set off and got a puncture. We couldn't repair it so we walked.

As we walked we thought we saw some dogs but they were wild, black, aggressive sheep. The whole herd ran after us. We ran as fast as we could. Finally the sound of hooves disappeared, we slowed down and walked home.

We got home and repaired the puncture but never told anybody about it.

Dan Cox (10)
Escrick CE Primary School

A Day In The Life Of A Young Wizard

I woke up, I didn't want to. I wanted to stay under my sheets for ever half asleep in the morning light. But I knew I couldn't because I had to do my morning lessons, charms (stupid), transfiguration (boring), potions (what's the point). Groaning I stepped out of bed and stuck. 'Alright,' I shouted across the boys' bedroom, 'who conjured magic goo again?' I pulled out my wand, waved it and the gooey substance (what a long word) disappeared. I couldn't be bothered to get dressed but I would have to. I couldn't trust my magic. I stumbled like an angered blind man down the steps to the great hall where we have breakfast. I found, and I am not lying, frogs in my cereal! After I had finished taking the disgusting creatures out of my breakfast there was no time to actually eat it. The bell had rung for morning lessons and I just could not be late.

I will not bother to tell you of what happened in the first morning lesson (potions). Let's just say I left in a huff, after being told I was a brain dead idiot. So here I am now, in the head's office. So far I have only written lines and had a 'serious' talk and it's taken over three hours. Wait a moment, yes! The head's letting me go, but I've got to stay in my room for the rest of the day. Oh well, things could be worse. So here I am sitting in my room dying of boredom but I have just found something that although is insulting, I find it very amusing. It is a letter, unnamed of course, it says, 'Quit while you're ahead or in your case behind.'
'Am I really that bad?' I wondered aloud.

Timothy Wulder (11)
Escrick CE Primary School

A Day In The Life Of My Pony

The cock crows . . .

Ravenous, he searches his stable for wisps of straw and hay. His jet-black eyes meet those of a kindly human, who gently slips a rope around his silky neck and leads him into the vast buttercup-filled paddock.

Lots on his mind, his equine brain, the size of a pea, he starts to devour the endless grass, savouring every blade . . .

A curious chicken, squat and plump, has taken time from egg-laying to make friends, but backs away as he coughs. But he is friendly, remembers the days when his hooves hurt him, a Jack Russell had come to visit him for hours . . .

The birds are singing, it is scorching, so he lowers himself and rolls, cooling himself and remembering . . .

After drinking a little, he dreams . . . no mares of the night had visited them . . .

He wakes, hungrily eating the grass as 'Human' arrives, making reassuring noises and leading him into his stable, with fresh shavings, water, hay and mollychaff with carrots. Brushed, rug on, hugged and kissed he eats away . . .

'Night, night Henry.'

Happy to know he is loved, he whinnies to a friend, and thinks about hopes, ambitions and dreams and as he does, he gallops into the sunset.

India Hare (11)
Escrick CE Primary School

FA CUP FINAL

I woke up, the sun was shining. I got dressed into my Leeds United kit, I was in all white and up against Liverpool, the treble winners. I had number 8, Bedford. This was the toughest game of the season, what a cracker.

I got into my Mazda 626, M reg and began to drive off to Cardiff a six mile journey. When I got there we started playing, Dacourt passed to me, I chipped the ball to Viduka, he headed it in the goal. Yes! We scored in seven seconds. The crowd went crazy! Then Fowler to Gerrard on the volley. What a goal! Hit the bar, hit the line and went in, Martyn had no chance. Kewell lays it off to Bowyer who has a shot. Yes! It is in but it is offside. No! Ferdinand passes to me, I chip it to Smith who lays it off to me. I have a shot, the goalkeeper saves it. Corner. Ian Harte takes it, it bounces in front of me and an overhead kick. What a goal. The whistle blows, we have won the FA Cup. The crowd go crazy. We lift the cup. What a day. I will get loads of money.

Edward Bedford (10)
Escrick CE Primary School

A DAY IN THE LIFE OF HARRY POTTER

I woke up with a start. It was midnight and someone was in my room. I fumbled about for my wand, then I picked it up. 'Lumos,' I shouted. A slither of light fell out of my wand. I cold just see an outline of Professor McGonagall. She had a look of terror on her face. She wandered over to me and said that Voldermort had been sighted in the castle.

'It's only Saturday morning and Voldermort's set out to kill me,' I told Ron as we walked out of the great hall. After giving Ron a third game of chess we set of to Hogsmeade the local wizarding village. Firstly we went to Zoncoes to buy Fred and George some filibuster fireworks. After that we set off to Honeydukes, a sweet shop. We spent half an hour picking sweets like, Exploding Rolos, Acid Slugs, Strawberry Tooth Shrinker and toffee. But as the lady weighed up the toffees one grew and grew until Voldermort had appeared, 'Expeliarmass,' he said. Ron's wand shot out of his hand -
'Avordacaabra,' I shouted. There was a flash of green light and a rush of wind and Voldermort died.

We legged it back to the castle to tell our news.

Tristan Watson (10)
Escrick CE Primary School

A Day In The Life Of Me

I woke up and jumped out of bed. 'Yippee!' I shouted. It was the day of my Egyptian school trip, and I couldn't wait. I pulled on my jeans and a white baggy T-shirt, because it was no school uniform - hooray!

I belted downstairs and grabbed a bowl of sticky chocolate cornflakes. 'Beep-beep!' the bus was here so I yelled goodbye to my mum, grabbed my packed lunch and scrambled onto the bus and found my best friend Clara to sit next to for the one hour journey.

We finally arrived at ten o'clock and started the tour.
'I need the loo,' I said to Mrs Kay.
'Again?' said Mrs Kay 'we'll meet you by the tombs.'
'I did drink two 500ml bottles of water at breaktime,' I replied and scampered off.

'Pharaoh's Tombs ahead,' I read out loud and then followed the path around. I turned a corner and saw a tomb making a funny noise. I climbed inside to investigate only to be sucked up by a big gush of wind. I went round and round, spinning this way and that, seeing different greens and blues.

Thud!

I finally landed next to Tutankhamun who was praying in Egyptian and being asked to put his death mask on. As I did so the wind came again and took me back to my class . . . Phew!

Sophie Quarmby (11)
Escrick CE Primary School

A DAY IN THE LIFE OF SAM ATKINSON

FA Cup Final:

I woke up and said to myself 'It's the FA Cup Final today, kick off at 7.30pm - great!'

The teams that are playing today are Leeds United v Manchester United; I am a sub for Leeds. I got changed and ran into the Millennium Stadium. It was time for kick-off, the team took the centre and the crowd roared.

Roy Keane, taking the centre with Andy Cole. Keane passed to Scholes, Scholes passed to Beckham. Beckham slips and got a yellow card, Ian Harte takes the free kick. He won a shot to Smith; Smith crosses it in for Kewell as he heads it into the back of the net. They take the centre, Cole passed back to Beckham and Beckham shoots and scores from the six yard box. It is one all!

The whistle blew, I was brought on for Robbie Keane and it is time for penalties.

Smith was taking the first penalty - his legs were shaking and he scores what was a wonderful goal!

The next penalty is David Beckham's - can he score? Yes, he scored! Ian Harte took the next penalty, you can tell he was nervous, he shoots then he scores a great penalty. Andy Cole was shaking - then he hits the post. *It's all over!* The crowd roared! The score was . . .

Sam Atkinson (11)
Escrick CE Primary School

THE DAY IN THE LIFE OF HOLLY (MY DOG)

I woke up and got out of my fluffy dog bed. I was very very excited because mum was going to take me into the woods. I had a gulp of my water and then started tugging and scratching at the door. Mum burst through and asked me what was the matter, I just barked happily.

We started to walk to the woods, I was pulling so much my mum fell over. When we got there, mum let me off the lead . . . I ran and ran and ran; this was the best day of my life.

Mum got my favourite ball out of her coat pocket and threw it. After about three throws, she threw it again and I chased after my red ball. I was stuck . . . something had got my back right leg. Mum called me but after a while she went home and decided to wait for me there.

Luckily a neighbour I knew was walking through the woods as well, I barked for help and he came up to me and untangled me from which turned out to be a pile of nettles - ouch! Anyway he took me home and mum was relieved.

I went to bed and thought to myself that I had lost my favourite ball but at least I was home with my family.

Jayne-Leigh Johnson (11)
Escrick CE Primary School

A DAY IN THE LIFE OF MY DOG!

I woke up and climbed out of my bed, my lovely woven basket bed with my name woven in different colours on it. Off I trotted down the stairs to look for my dog bowl.

Ahh the sweet smell of Pedigree dog biscuits I thought to myself. Also the sweet smell of bacon . . . bacon . . . do I smell bacon? I ran like a tornado into the kitchen to find the sizzling bacon in my bowl.
'Heaven!' I thought. It was a bit burnt but I gobbled it up and away. Then said my goodbyes to the kids. After about five minutes of chasing my tail I heard a call -

'Walkies!' It was Dad! 'Come on Cindy, walkies!'

I hurried into the room where dad was.

After a ten minute walk in the woods, dad's feet were getting tired, I can always tell with dad because he starts to moan and curse things like twigs and trees.

'Stupid tree!' He muttered, 'why can't you be like the rest of the trees and not have so many roots!' I decided that this meant that he wanted a rest. He sat down on the roots of the tree, then picked up a twig. 'Here girl, fetch!' He said as he lifted the twig into the air.

I watched the half dead twig fly through the air and the next thing I knew I was in the middle of the woods. I did not know this place. Dad hadn't walked me here ever before. I walked around but stayed close to where I first realised that I was *lost!*

Off I trotted north (well I think it was north, or was it west?) to find the tree where dad was sitting. But wait, he wasn't there. I'm sure that is the tree ahead on the footpath and after running hard, my legs started to get tired.

But then I saw a figure . . .

Was it dad or not?

I ran towards the figure only to find it was a scarecrow! I felt so dim. But wait a minute, I was on the right track. Here was where I had slipped in the puddle earlier and where I went to the loo! And . . . yes it's . . . the car park - bliss! *Dad* is here, *hooray!* I was found.

Lydia McCool (10)
Escrick CE Primary School

A DAY IN THE LIFE OF JAYNE JOHNSON

I woke up and I moaned, this was going to be the worst day of my life. I got out of bed and looked at myself in the mirror, I looked a complete mess. I went to get my hair gel but I knocked it over. 'Oh no!' I knew it was going to be a bad day.

When I got to school that day I was soaking because it was raining cats and dogs. I was late so I got yelled at by Miss Wilks. I went over to my friend Emily Anderson 'Hi Emily!' I mouthed to her, but she turned away, she was not my friend now.

'Now everyone, today we are going on a school trip, pick your partner and off we go!' Our teacher. Miss Wilks bellowed. I had no partner so I had to go with my enemy - Hanna Wade.

At Eden camp (which was our school trip) I didn't approve of my group. They only did things they wanted to do, they were always excluding me and whispering about me, but soon they began to become strangely nice.

'Do you want to play 'dares' with us, Jayne?' said Sophie.
I asked what she wanted me to do . . .
'Just go through that door!' said Hanna.
I did as I was told, because I didn't fancy a fallout/loss of friends.
I went through the door
I stopped breathing . . .

'Mummy, mummy that thing is moving!' said a young girl.

I had walked into the blitz experience!

It was really dark and scary and, and . . . my class walked through

'Get out now!' screamed Miss Wilks.

Not quite knowing what to do, the girls-who were supposed to be my friends - smirked viciously.

Back to school . . . I was in deep trouble!

I had had a bad day.

Clara J Smowton (10)
Escrick CE Primary School

A DAY IN THE LIFE OF A VIKING LADY

I woke up suddenly as I heard the banging and clattering of my husband making his work tools out of stone. As I clambered out of my very uncomfortable bed I was reminded of the day ahead . . .

Firstly there was breakfast to make and lunch to prepare. After that I have to start making my tools. A sword, a spear, an arrow and a bow which we need to kill the animals which we eat. I also have to make our pots for cooking with and for eating from. I also have to help my husband when we go out hunting for food.

In the woods when we go hunting, we lay lots of traps for the animals. We have to throw our spears at the animals hoping they hit them. Any animals that we catch, we then take back to our cave.

To cook the food we catch, we make a fire, collect some sticks, hold skinned animal over the fire until it's cooked and ready to eat. Sometimes, if we are not too tired, we have a game of stone-carved chess. This is a very fun activity and our only form of entertainment. After playing chess we wind down and think about retiring to bed, after a long, long, hard busy day.

Katie Louise Doubtfire (10)
Gladstone Road Junior School

A Day In The Life Of Athena

I am Athena, Goddess of Art, war and wisdom. My symbols are the owl and the olive tree. I teach men to tame horses as well as Art.

I live on Mount Olympus. Zeus is god of all gods. He and his wife Hera are partying at the moment. Art considers patience, if not it turns into a disaster.

You must treat a horse properly otherwise it will kick you or become ill. As I walk, my golden dress follows on the shiny floor. I wake up to hear birds singing. Pictures, paintings and trophies surround me. My breakfast was tropical fruits and after my breakfast I finished my painting after yet teaching men to tame horses. When I had finished my painting I could still taste my breakfast in my throat. I had my lunch. Fruit again . . . so refreshing.

For a while I relaxed, I need to rest. An hour later I fed the horses, did some more sketching, and after that I ate some cranberries, mangoes and peaches I had a drop of wine as well.

I slipped into my dressing gown, I could faintly hear a harp playing, relaxing I lie on the bed, still hearing the musical instruments, I breathed wearily. Stars dotted up above, twinkling. Then I silently doze off zzz zzz.

Sarah Campleman (10)
Gladstone Road Junior School

A DAY IN THE LIFE OF LUDWIG VAN BEETHOVEN

Today I'm moving to Bonn in Vienna to see if I can become a composer and virtuoso pianist. I am very excited about it all.

Ever since my father gave me my first lesson in music I knew that it would become my life. Today I am making my dream come true to the extent that I will be a pupil of Haydn. I know he will help me to get where I want to be and I will give everything that I can.

Although I am excited, I know that there are many people out there who are so good at music. It scares me because I want to be as good as, if not better than them in my own right. I want people to listen to my music and know that the next piece they hear will be as clear to them as my name.

I want my music to be known throughout the world and to be listened to far into the future. I hope people of all ages will be able to have fond memories from it and that the music will help them to achieve something good in their lives.

Music is in my blood and it makes me very happy. I know that should I become a great composer, it is likely that my fame will come when I am dead. This does not matter, it gives me great comfort to know that whilst I am still here I am doing this for me and anything that comes out of it hopefully will benefit someone else.

Jarrod Dormer (10)
Gladstone Road Junior School

THE DAY IN THE LIFE OF A MAID

I lived in London and worked in a large house owned by a wealthy family. The job I got was as a maid which meant doing cooking, cleaning, ironing, carpet beating, washing and a lot, lot more.

I soon found out if I did anything wrong I got a bad telling off. I slept at the top of the house (which is now known as the attic). Three other maids also slept in this room. Our room was cold, dark and damp, it also had a leaky roof.

We were woken up at 6 o'clock and our first job was to clean and light the fires. Then help make and serve breakfast, after which we had to make the beds and empty the chamber pots.

One morning, the family told me to do the ironing and polish the silver. I was finding everything very very hard because the family were coming home soon and going to the opera.

The ironing was not complete so I was rushing around everywhere. I was doing the ironing when I realised there was a bit of silver that wasn't polished. I rushed over to do it and a few minutes later I smelled burning and found that there was a giant hole in the shirt so I hid it in the cupboard and when they got ready I was in so much trouble that I lost my job and my home.

Rachael Kay (9)
Gladstone Road Junior School

A Day In The Life Of A Victorian Maid

Oh wait, wait! Be strong! Good morning, I am Eleanor. I am a Victorian maid and I work for a rich family called the Mennels. I am so so tired. I have to get up at 3am and go to sleep at 9pm. That's 18 hours!

First on my agenda is to start breakfast along with three other maids called Anne, Louisa and Mary. Then I go and open all the windows, all 15 of them. I then have to go and wake up the family. What a job! And I have the bruises to prove it. Ouch!

Whilst the family are getting ready for breakfast, I am the one who has to go and scrape all the sweets that are stuck on the furniture . . . what a disgusting job! I then have to go and serve breakfast then get changed. Help the children, water the plants and dust the whole house. Then whilst the family are out, I have to clean and set the table for dinner. Then at last, the maids all get a break. We all spend time lying on our beds thinking what a horrible, disgusting and gruelling morning we've had.

Then came a great big slam!
It was our employers.

We had only been asleep for three hours, but it felt good. Oh well, back to another day of slaving around.

Louisa Pratt (10)
Gladstone Road Junior School

A DAY IN THE LIFE OF QUEEN VICTORIA

Today I got the most unusual surprise, my mother woke me up in the early morning to tell me that I had some visitors.

The Archbishop of Canterbury told me my uncle William VI had died late last night, so I am the Queen of England. He also told me that I would be crowned Queen later on in the day, I was very excited.

Time passed quickly enough and soon I was sat in front of hundreds of people in Westminster Abbey with a heavy robe on my back. Soon the guards had to close the door because the room was packed.

After I was crowned, trumpets started blowing and a parade started around London.

Laura Bolton (9)
Gladstone Road Junior School

A DAY IN THE LIFE OF APHRODITE

My mum and dad and I - Aphrodite. We are all slaves and we have to bring food and drink to the king. We have to go to the theatre to go and help the king.

I know I shouldn't go and see the animals get killed but I have to or I will also get killed because the king will not stand being treated like that. He thinks it's really funny and he demands to see it, but I like it when people sing and play lovely songs. Slaves also dance when they are about to go shopping.

One day two slaves fell in love and got married and that really touched me but then I woke up and I said to my mum 'Have you got any goddesses ?'
'Yes,' she said 'a goddess of wealth.'
'Come on! Come on! It's the great drama festival in honour of the goddess of wine and merry-making, that is where we are going.'

We had to go with the king, 100 slaves died this year and many animals got killed. Then the king went trading, he traded 100 slaves for a lot of pottery and metalwork's. Then 200 for a stone mansion and some were traded for jewellery.

The man was very lonely and sad and the lady she was a slave and she was sad also but the man went back to fetch her. I think it was love at first sight but they were just friends - but not if I have anything to do with it.

April Smith (10)
Gladstone Road Junior School

A Day In The Life Of A Victorian Maid

Oh my back! High and low every day.

Hello, I'm called Bethanny Smyth. I'm a maid and for me, well it's just work, work, work, never-ending work.

Oh gosh I'm not scrubbing the floor. Oh my back, it kills me. I wish I could get out of here, but I suppose it's better than begging on the cold streets of London and starving to death.

'Maid! Get here at once!'
'Yes madam, right away madam!'

That's my boss Madam Craven. She is really mean.
Her husband is at school as a headmaster. Mrs Craven is just taking over for now.

'Maid!'
'Coming madam!'
I hope she doesn't shout at me.
Please come with me to find out what my next job is.

'Here madam!'
'Clean that mat now!'

I get the beater and hang the mat on the washing line.
Wham, wham, wham. Oh my arm. I'm going to need Florence Nightingale next. Wham, wham, wham.

'Maid that will do. Get on with the dishes. Make my tea and make Master Craven's soup. Chop chop, you haven't go all day you know!'

Slam!
I'm glad she's gone.
Do this and do that like I say.
Work, work, work.
Got to go bye, bye!

Bethanny Smyth (9)
Gladstone Road Junior School

A DAY IN THE LIFE OF A VICTORIAN MAID!

Morning:

Every morning I wake up at 6am to do my morning job. It's hard work doing this job, I make beds, clean up, put the clothes in the washing machine and make the food. I get paid five shillings. Sometimes I have to take photos of very rich people or families who came to stay in this building.

Lunchtime:

At lunchtime, I make lunch for everyone in the building. There are other maids that help me in this place and they are called Louise, Victoria and Susanne. I'm called Sarah.

Afternoon:

We have our break for two hours. We have lunch at home and we can see our children. I have one boy called Sam, he's eight now.

Family:

Sam's dad is called Craig. My mum and dad are called Jemma and Paul. John my brother is 21 and I am 23. Sam likes history and English. He also likes his teacher Mrs Ashwell.

Evening:

I make the dinner, Susanne does the desserts. My brother John works as a waiter between 5.30pm and 9.30pm.

Night time:

I make sure people are cosy in their beds, I go to bed at midnight and I get six hours sleep.

Disgusting matters:

(1) There are snakes in our garden.
(2) People always get drunk at night time.

Holly Crocker (10)
Gladstone Road Junior School

A DAY IN THE LIFE OF SABRINA

I woke up really early. The sun was streaming in through the windows.
I went downstairs still in my pyjamas, I looked down and saw my
clothes. I couldn't go into the other realm like this! I watched my finger,
zap! I wore a white belly-top and jeans. 'Cool!' I thought.

I went back upstairs after I'd had some breakfast. My aunts wanted me
to go to the other realm to see Drell the head of the Witches Council,
and ask if I could go forward in time to see what I could do. My aunts
were worried that because I am half mortal, I won't be able to do a lot
of witches things.

I got to the linen closet 'Bye Sabrina!' I heard from Salem, and 'Good
luck!' said my aunts in unison.

I forced my hand to the doorknob, I stepped in, my feet trembling.
Colours whirled around me 'The Witches Council, the Witches
Council' I repeated. I stopped with a thud. I opened a door and there
before me was a smartly dressed man wearing a horrible fake smile.
'Congratulations!' he shouted 'You are our two millionth customer!
You win this fabulous board game! Now go away, you won't want
anything else from us!'

I walked away. What should I do? It looked quite cool actually.

I went to my best friend Valerie's house and showed her the game.
'Which witch is which? Sounds like a freaky game to me!'
Valerie is a mortal.
'So well, let's play, shall we?' I asked.
'Alright!' said Valerie.

After a while the trouble began. Valerie landed on a switch magic
square.

'What does this mean?' she asked.

I wasn't the only one who lost my powers, so did Aunt Zelda. So now
Valerie and Salem have magical powers. What happened is that little
specks of magic went through the air. Valerie shook, so did Salem.

We stopped playing the game about a minute later, nothing drastic happened.

'Can I go home please Sabrina?' Val asked 'I'm feeling weird.'
'Okay' I said hurrying her off.

Next morning I got a phone call.
'Hey Sabrina? I wanted a bowl of cornflakes this morning, well I wanted a slave, and I was waving my finger about and well, bang! You won't belie . . .' she said.
I cut her off 'He was there?'
'Well yeah - see ya!' Now she was hurrying off.

I decided to look at the game. On the bad squares were 'Switch magic', 'Are you scared yet?' and 'Boo!' I carried on looking until I came to a 'Switch back square.' Yes!

I got dressed and went downstairs, what was that smell? I went into the kitchen. Urgh!

Thousands of fish were flipping about and Salem was rolling around. 'This is the life!' he cried.

After school I phoned Val 'Come on Val,' I said, 'please, please, please. Please play the game!' I pleaded.

'Oh alright! But I feel really bad since I played it last.'

Val came after school and we played.
After a while I landed on the switch-back squares. Yes!
When she'd gone, I tried a spell.

Zap, zap I'm thirsty now.
Give me orange juice kapow!

Lame, I know but it worked!

Val phoned 'Oh my goodness Sabrina! My slave *melted!*' She yelled.

'Er . . . it's all in your mind.'
Ha huh! I thought it up as I went along.

I love my powers, and at least the house doesn't smell of fish anymore.

Laura Chapman (10)
Greasbrough J&I School

A Day In The Life Of A Dolphin Under The Sea

One summer's day, Daisy the dolphin and Daphne the dolphin were playing hide and seek when Jennifer the jellyfish came up from her house.

'Can I play with you?' she asked.

'Of course you can,' said Daisy.

'Can I count please,' said Jenny.

'Yes,' said Daphne.

Jenny counted to a hundred.

'Ready or not, here I come,' said Jenny loudly.

'Found Daphne, found you, Daisy.'

'I'm hungry, are you?'

'Yes I am.'

'Let's go to Larry Lobster's Blue Ocean Cafe.'

'OK then.'

They all had seaweed salad and a drink of cockleshell juice.

'How much will that be, Larry?' asked Jenny.

'That will be five clams please.'

'OK.'

Jenny paid two clams, Daphne paid two clams and Daisy paid one clam.

Next they went to get some clams from the Sandy Shore Bank. They each got twenty-five clams to go to Stacey Seahorse's Top Shop. It was the only shop in Shellrock Village. It sold absolutely everything, clothes CDs, food, drink and lots of other things too. At about three o'clock they went to the Top Shop. When they got there they all split up. Daisy bought a purple dress. In the middle of it there was a pattern of a flower made of beads and she bought a CD of the Shellrock Band. Daphne bought a blue silk dress and a pink top. Jenny bought a teddy bear, a doll, a hoop, oh and a swimming pool. When they got home, they all had tea then they went to bed. They were the best of friends after that.

Rachel France (9)
Greasbrough J&I School

IN A WORLD OF BUMBLESNOUTS

'It's my turn,' said Tony (one of the Bumblesnouts, green with red spots).

'It's my turn to move the chest.'

'No, it's not!' said Kevin nastily. 'It's my turn, not yours!'

'No it's not!'

'Yes it is!'

'No it's . . . !'

'Quit! Quit!' said Emma interrupting. 'You can't argue especially when we're going on holiday.'

'I suppose she's right,' said Kevin. 'But it's my turn,' said Kevin immediately.

'No it's not,' said Tony.

'It's mine.'

'No it's not, it's mine.'

'It's not.'

'It is.'

'Shush, shush!' said Emma. 'We've got to go and pack.'

'OK,' said Kevin, 'I'll put the chest away.'

'But,' said Tony immediately, 'just remember it is mine.'

Tony and Emma looked exactly the same and Kevin was the odd one out because he was red with orange spots. When everybody had finished, they set off for the airport to go to Tenerife.

'Well,' said Emma (because she was the oldest), 'we are going to to a table, a table saying who's going to pick where we are going first.'

'Oh please, please, pick me,' said Tony.

'OK' said Emma. 'It'll be Tony then me, then you, Kevin.'

'Emma, you should go last, you're the oldest.'

'Exactly,' said Emma. 'I'm the oldest, so I should pick where I want to go on the table.'

'I suppose,' said Kevin.

'Can I pick now?' asked Kevin.

'OK,' said Emma.

'I want to go to the beach first.'

'Great!' said Kevin and Emma together. 'I was going to pick that anyway.'

'Stop copying!'

On the beach they built sand castles, went for a swim and everything you do at the beach.

'Can we have an ice cream now?' asked Tony (what Emma promised him an hour ago). So they had an ice cream and then it was Emma's turn. They went to a swimming pool and Emma sunbathed. Then it was Kevin's turn. He wanted to go to the fair. They went on all sorts of rides. Then it was time for them to go back to space.

Nicolle Hobson (10)
Greasbrough J&I School

THE NIGHTMARE

She was walking alone. The forest was deep and dark. She heard twigs snapping, but they were only foxes running. Suddenly she was grabbed from behind. She tried to fight it, but couldn't. Finally she got away. Seconds later, it happened again. Again she escaped. She was screaming.

'No! Oh no, no, no!'

The terror was repeated, each time getting worse. Her attacker was getting stronger. He said something. Kath was scared. She knew he would never go away.

A few minutes later he was back. This time he was really big and strong. She kicked him and started to run. She was running round and round in circles; each time she was returning to the same spot, and the same thing was happening. She screamed trying to get out.

She found herself back at the same spot. He was bigger and stronger still.

He said, 'You'll never make it out alive.'

Kath screamed, *'Help!'*

He laughed. It was a wicked laugh.

'No! No! No! Get off me, get off me!' she yelled.

'Kath, calm down. It's me, Brendan.' Her husband walked in.

'Oh, Brendan. I've just had the most terrifying nightmare. The thing, it seemed so real,' Kath sobbed. 'Look! I've got scratches on my arm from where I tried to get away. I was really frightened. I thought I'd never get out alive.'

'You'll be alright. I promise.' sighed Brendan.

Katie Harber (10)
Heath View Community Primary School

THE MURDER

'I know where you are, Sara,' said the murderer.
Gunshots fired, and Sara was dead on the floor.

'Have you got any leads?' asked Ken.
The door slammed open and Kath appeared, stroking a revolver the size of her hand, and puffing on a cigar.
'Show me the pictures!'
'Who are these?' Ken enquired.
'My undercover agents, Andy and Andy, aka Skin Head and Gingerbeard.'
'Jo, show them to the conference room.'
'OK' said Jo, haughtily.
'These are the first sightings of him,' said Ken.
'Have you got any pictures of him without a balaclava on?' Kath asked sarcastically.
'Yes, just one of him holding three people hostage.'
'I know him from somewhere,' said Skin Head.
'We have had some news that he will be in the hotel.'
'Right then, let's go,' said Kath loading her gun.

'Right, now what do we do?' asked Skin Head.
'You sit down here and wait until he comes,' said Kath.

'You wanted me?' said the murderer.
'Yes,' said Skin Head.
'Well I don't want you,' said the murderer.
He pulled a gun from his coat. Shots fired and Skin Head screamed as the bullet entered his leg.

The murderer started running. Kath chased him. Chairs fell as she hurdled over tables. Cornering the villain she shot him in the leg.
'I hate you,' said the murderer in a dying voice.

It is easier to kill pigs than you, you doggie-do face!' said Kath.
'I thought you liked pigs,' Gingerbeard whispered with his final breath.

Matthew Hainsworth (10
Heath View Community Primary School

A DAY IN THE LIFE OF THE SUN

Dear Shooting Star

I woke up today and gave a huge or ginormous yawn. *Oops* I think that's what caused the earthquake in Tokyo! Well I woke up and felt alive, free and jolly . . . well actually I felt a bit fed up, a bit sticky, a bit damp in a way, a bit down basically. I realised I had a runny nose, I wanted to stay in bed. I really did. But I had to go to work. *I had to go!*
I don't get paid either so that makes me very grumpy and that's not all. In this tiny Milky Way, guess what? Earthlings are exploring! They are really bugging me, but definitely Miss Moon. Did you know she sometimes cries? That's why there's a lot of rain. Well it's none of her business what's on her and Mars you know.

Me and Earth had a bit of a chat today.
She told me, 'Yeah, foot and smelly mouth is really horrendous on here!'
'What's that?' I asked.
'Well, it's where animals have to be killed.'
I still don't know what it is, do you? And what's your favourite season? Mine's summer! I just love it! I put on my shades and boogie! I do get a bit worried sometimes when I give Earthlings a heat rash, but it serves them right for disturbing Miss Moon! What do you think? Well bye, I'm going to sleep in the west.

Sun!

Emilia Slezak (10)
Hempland Primary School

A Day In The Life Of A Dog

Hi, my name is Max and I am a dog. I am very popular around here for trouble.

The other day I was in the garden. I was having a lot of fun until I heard Miss Smith's dogs, Sam and Ben. It sounded as if they were having more fun than I was.

So I went to see what it was all about. I pinched their ball. They began to chase me so I ran.

Then Miss Smith started to chase. It ended up with the whole street after me. But I burst the ball and got home in time for supper.

Then I saw Miss Smith coming up the drive. I dashed out of the house. Guess what I got up to . . .

Alannah Gatford (10)
Hempland Primary School

A Day In The Life Of A Lion!

8.00am - Wake up and have an early zebra and buffalo breakfast, come back from hunting at 9.00am then laze in the sun.

10.00am - Wake up cubs for breakfast.

10.30am - Clean up the cubs after eating, then lie in the sun.

11.45am - Go hunting for an hour then come back to eat lunch with everyone.

1.30pm - Have a walk around the plains of Africa with the family.

2.30pm
Lie in the sun for an hour and a half.

4.00pm - Go hunting, bring the food back for the family in one hour, lie in the sun to digest the food.

7.30pm - Put the cubs to bed and I stay awake to guard the family, normally something would attack them so I try and fight it off. Humans normally pitch tents around us.

11.30pm - Go out for a zebra and jackal for a midnight feast with my wife.

After that we'll go to sleep. About one hour later the humans would try catching us so we go and rip their tents to pieces, and the humans of course.

2.30am - Try and get back to sleep.

5.00am
Buffalo try to attack my family so we all get up and fight them off.

Josh Douglas (10)
Hempland Primary School

A DAY IN THE LIFE OF A FIVE POUND NOTE

Hi! I'm Freddie the five pound note and I am going to tell you about what happened on 2nd July, the day that I would never forget.

It was a lovely summer's day and my friends and I were relaxing in the safe in the bank. Suddenly we heard a voice, as ferocious as thunder.
'Hand over all the money or everyone in this bank gets it!'
The lady cashier nervously ran to the safe and picked me and the other notes up, put us in a bag and gave us to the robber. Then she got my little friends, the pound coins out.
'That's all,' she stuttered.
He hurried out. Waiting in a red BMW were two men. The robbers got into the car and drove away. They stopped in the middle of a deserted car park and counted us. We all added up together to make £500,000. Then they started to argue.
'I want £10,000,' yelled one man.
'No, you can't have that much, I want £400,000.'
It was better than a pantomime!

Suddenly the biggest man pushed the other two men out of the car and drove off. Not looking where he was going, the robber crashed into a fruit and vegetable stall. Unfortunately he had forgotten to lock the boot and me and the other notes came tumbling out. We landed on the road. Two men passing by grabbed the man and phoned the police. They arrived five minutes later. They arrested the man and returned us to the bank.

At last we were safe! Home sweet home!

Rachel Pilmoor (10)
Hempland Primary School

A Day In The Life Of A Girl In An Orphanage

As I wake up the first thing I see is my photo of my parents when I was one year old. I look and I think,

'I wonder if they will ever come and take me and live happily every after.'

Then I remember happily ever after is only in fairy tales.

Ding, dong, there goes the wake up bell. I know it is Kate (my social worker) ringing the bell, because she always rings the bell four times. As usual it is 7.30 in the morning.

I dress as fast as I can and sprint downstairs to see if I am first down there and can possibly get 'Queen Chair' as I named it. It is *really* comfy, and you can see the TV really well! *Yes* I have done it for the fourth time in four days! I turn on to channel one to see if Zappoblast is on, when, oh no, here comes Jess, Lucy and Mary, the biggest bullies on planet Earth.

'Eew, look here is Josie, the idiot who thinks her mum and dad are alive and will come for her,' whines Jess.

Jess is always winding me up, whenever she has the chance. Like last week she, well I will not go into that. *And* now she is teasing me about my parents!

'You stay silent about my parents, I bet you I will get collected from them and live a brilliant life,' I reply.

I get a great feeling when I stand up to that *idiot!* Katie comes in so they sneak off. Typical! They are always getting away with this.

'I have some great news for you today, Josie, there has been an offer of a foster home. They are a really nice couple with one child and you seem to be what they are looking for and would like to know if you could move in next week!'

'Yes, I would love to! Cool!' I scream.

Maddy Leftwich (10)
Hempland Primary School

A Day In The Life Of A Dartmoor Pony

My name is Breeze, I have chocolate brown eyes, a flowing mane and a velvety nose. My coat is a deep brown.

When I awoke, the sky was pink scattered with brilliant orange. I knew it was early morning. My herd awoke and we began to graze.

Our leader, a fierce stallion by the name of Hoofbeat was grazing too, but his eyes were up, alert, scanning for signs of danger. That's a leader's job; to protect his herd. Soon Hoofbeat called our herd to order, I took my place. We set off to find new
pastures, our hooves beating across the grass.

After a time, we began to slow down. I craned my neck forwards to see what was going on. Then I saw what was the matter. There, standing before us, was our worst enemy, *man.* I'd been told about man - how they capture you and make you work for them. It's enough to make your blood run cold.

I stood there, paralysed with fear, when Hoofbeat's whinny brought me to my senses.
'Gallop,' he cried.
We set off at a lightning pace away from the man. I was galloping as fast as I could go, pushing myself on. Eventually we slowed down and entered a cave. It was vast and dark but cosy. As I lay down, sweat was dripping down my neck, my flanks were heaving.

As I lie here now, I think:
'I made it this time but will I make it the next?'

Rachael West (10)
Hempland Primary School

24 HOURS WITH ME

I wake up, get dressed, go tot he toilet and there is someone in there.
I ask 'Who's there?'
It's my brother. He takes his time and comes out in a lazy way and then
I go to sleep on the floor and when I wake up it's nine o'clock and I
quickly look for my socks and put my shoes on. And I don't have time
to eat so I go to school and get yelled at by the teachers for eating gum.
Then I have to do a hundred lines.

Then I eat dinners that are worms, slugs, spiders and frogs for pudding
(joke). Then I do my English and have a fight. The teacher sends me to
early years unit and I play with the babies and I act like one. Then I go
home and I get chased by a dog named Joe. I jump on the wall and the
dog tries to get up but it is too small. I throw a stick far away and it goes
to get it, but, by the time it comes back, I have gone home.

Then I go to the shops and I ask,
'How much is a chocolate bar?'
They say 'Forty pence.'
So I say, 'In the other shops they are cheaper.'
They give it to me for thirty pence.

Aboobakar Altaf (10)
Leopold Primary School

A DAY IN THE LIFE OF DARNELLE

On Sunday 18th February 2001, my little baby brother was born. He is called Darnelle. My mum came out of hospital on the 22nd. When I went home he kept my mum up every night and she was very tired. I had to help her a lot.

The next day I was at school so I did not see a lot of him. When I got home he was sleeping. The only things he did were eat, sleep, drink and smile. After six weeks he could see everything. He always cried and wanted my mum.

At two months he did his first giggle. He always talks in baby language. If you say 'Yes he did,' he really will talk back in his baby words.
I think he is going to talk and walk when he is nine months. He tries to talk and walk, he does not crawl, but will walk first.

At three months, Darnelle is turning over on the bed. He is meant to turn over at four months. Over the past months, my life has changed completely. I'm so happy and joyful and my mum is so happy we now have three people in our house.

Melissa Bennett (10)
Leopold Primary School

A Day In The Life Of My Sister

One day I was in the corridor. In the dark my baby sister was playing on the stairs. I went and carried her and took her into my bedroom. I made her sleep. After a while she got dressed and went out to play. She got tired so I gave her milk and made her go to sleep.

And then, in the morning, she got dressed. Then I gave her breakfast. She played around and went under the table, and upstairs, and into my room. I went up and carried her.

Then I brought her downstairs and into the sitting room. I made her lie down to get her nappy off and put the other nappy on. Then I switched on the TV for her. she watched cartoons then she started crying. So I picked her up and gave her a toy to play with. Afterwards I took her onto the grass and I played with her. She ran and ran as far as she could. She sometimes fell over. Soon she fell over and cried so I picked her up and put a plaster on her arm. Soon she went out of the gate, I played with my doll and sometimes she picked some stones and threw them on the floor.

Then I picked her up and went to give her milk. Then she slept and slept. She woke up and she started crying. I ran upstairs and carried her into the kitchen. Then I put her down and started helping my mum. Soon she opened the kitchen door and went into the sitting room.

After a while my dad came home and said,
'Let's go somewhere.'
'Okay,' we said.
So I carried her and put her coat on and I took her in the car. As soon as I put her in the car, she started playing with my doll.

Shumaila Jubble (10)
Leopold Primary School

198

A DAY IN THE LIFE OF JOHNNY

Johnny wakes up, eats breakfast and goes out and plays football with his brother. Then he goes shopping for his mum then he goes to town to buy tickets for himself.

When he comes back he starts to fight with the children, then he goes inside.

Then Johnny comes out and goes to the shop and buys some sweets, crisps and chocolate. When he comes back he starts to swear at people and the people throw stones, wrappers and sticks at him.

Then Johnny goes in and tells his brother, and his brother goes out and tells everyone to stop throwing stones.

Then Johnny goes in for two hours and after two hours he and his brother and his mum go to the airport in a car to get his sister who has just come from India.

When they get home, Johnny goes out and starts to play football.

After a while, this boy called Ben comes out and Johnny starts to swear at him. Ben gets mad and gets his dog out to chase Johnny, and Johnny goes round and round. Then he goes in, drinks milk and goes to sleep.

Ans Aslam (10)
Leopold Primary School

A DAY IN THE LIFE OF A HEDGEHOG

6.30am - The hedgehog plods about to shampoo his curly bristles, dries his bristles then goes downstairs to get some oatmeal.

7.00am - He gets his raincoat on then goes out. It's really hot so he takes his coat off and puts it in his pocket, thinks about his bed, then walks.

7.30am - He's hungry so Hedgy goes into Hedgedonalds to get some cress fries and watercress tomato nuggets.

8.00am - Starts to head to his hairdresser's, opens it, sorts out the permed, curled, plaited, blondish-brown extensions.

8.30am - Someone comes in, it's Shante. She wants curled black extensions.

9.00am - He's finished, closes up the shop then walks up to the library.

9.30am - He gets there and goes to get some books.

10.00am - He's got five atlases, borrows them and goes home.

10.30am - He walks over the road, then *splat!* He's knocked dead.

11.00am - Then in Heaven he eats some fried slugs before he gets his golden diamond halo.

11.30am - Presentation of hairdressing styles. Everyone comes out of the room with haircuts.

12.00pm - Time for witchcraft! Hedgy magics all the luggage away.

12.30pm - Lunchtime for juniors. Hedgy gets some spaghetti and French bread with Bolognese, dessert: vanilla ice cream, drink; Lilt.

1.00pm - Nap time. Hedgy doesn't sleep he does his duties. He practises DJing.

1.30pm - Nap time for Hedgy. He gets his pjs on, gets his teddy and sleeps.

He sleeps till next day (lazy bones).

Chama Mwape (10)
Leopold Primary School

THE DAY IN A LIFE OF A PYTHON

I woke up in the morning, and went into my bowl of water to bathe. It was just the right temperature for me. I was shedding my skin. It was very loose.

I was thinking about my lovely rats on the top of my vavarium. I could hear the man coming to feed me. I saw him take a rat, my mouth was watering. I could taste it already!

Then the cage opened and he dropped the rat in front of me. I couldn't control my body, it just moved at the rat. I opened my mouth and swallowed it whole. It took me a while to digest it. Ummmm! It was lovely.

After I had eaten my rat I had a lay down and coiled myself up and settled down under my light on my heat mat, my skin was coming off even more. It was more than ¾ of the way off now. The man got me out of my vavarium and took me out into the garden for some fresh air. He didn't let me go, I just coiled round his arm and then he took me back inside.

I didn't want to go back in my vavarium so I turned away from it but then it got boring so I went back in and got in the water bowl to have a bathe. Then my skin came off and the man came to look at me and saw my skin. He opened my vararium and got it out. He put it on my vararium on the top. I went under my light and went to sleep.

David Bogg (10)
Ley Top Primary School

The Day In The Life Of My Dog Bruno

8.00am Wake up (yawn). Oh hello Sarah, any toast crust left? Oh none left.

9.00am Mum, Mum! Pleeeaase let me out.

9.05am Aaahh! That's better.

10.00am Oy get off me Kyle, I'm trying to get warm in front of the fire.

11.00am Mum's going out, let's hope she gets me a nice juicy marrow-filled large bone. I'd better stop making myself drool.

11.30am Mmm! Leave me alone I'm eating a nice juicy bone from Mum.

12.00pm Sarah's coming home soon I can sense her, I'm off out to keep myself amused with Jasper.

1.00pm I'm off to Chellow Dene later with all the lads.

3.00pm Sarah's home, only Lisa and Tilk to wait for.

5.00pm I'm running down the field (splash). Brr! This water's cold, I'm getting out.

6.00pm Just sitting in the sunset to dry off.

7.00pm Mum's going to work. She'll be back at eleven.

8.00pm Sarah's playing the PlayStation. I'll stare at myself in the mirror.

10.00pm Dad's turning the fire on, warmth here I come!

12.00am I'm off to bed so I'll see you in the morning!

Sarah Doherty (11)
Ley Top Primary School

THE DAY IN THE LIFE OF A TEASPOON

I live in a drawer, a dirty dusty smelly drawer. Do my owners really think I like living in a drawer surrounding my neighbours who are really not nice people. Let's start with Mr Freddie Fork. Now I really have to tell you about this guy. To start with he is extremely dirty. I mean, I don't blame him or anything, it's our owners that don't clean us properly, but with his sharp ends you'd think that he'd stab them and give them a clue.

Next is Mr Kit Knife, he can be really nice but he does have a sharp side to him. I told him the other day that he wasn't as clean as he could be and he stabbed me right in the handle and it nearly hit me near the mouth. I can tell you.

I have lots of other neighbours too but they are in their own little group and I hope they stay there too. I think Mrs T Opener has a fancy for Mr R Pin but then he is smooth talking and all the girls in this group all get taken in by him, but not me.

Anyway, I must tell you that my experience yesterday was horrible. Well I managed to move to the bottom of the drawer and I wasn't noticed for weeks until yesterday my owner must of been in a good mood to have cleaned the drawer out, it wasn't a good experience because they chucked us in this hot soapy water and then ten minutes later they made yet another cup of tea and so I was yet again in hot water. I wouldn't mind that so much, but it's those horrible cheap tea bags, they get right up my nose.

Now it's time to go and dream about ice cubes. Ohh, what a life they lead. Ohh, there I go moaning again, but after all it is my job and how long do you think anyone can keep for, without losing it.

Katy Gillingham (11)
Ley Top Primary School

A DAY IN THE LIFE OF MOSES

7.05am Wake up, tired from last night. The slave has come in with breakfast - mmm . . . corn, bread with honey and water. It is a nice day today, I think I'll take a walk around the market and buy a new pair of sandals.

10.00am Ready to go, I'm dressed and I've had my breakfast, I think I'll see how Dad's new pyramid is coming on. You won't believe what I'm watching, an Egyptian guard hitting a Jewish slave.

11.30am I can stand it no longer, I run up to the Egyptian guard, take out my knife and, oh what have I done? I've killed him. I run away before anyone had seen what I'd done. I shouldn't have done it. Will God ever forgive me?

4.30pm I am in the middle of nowhere and hungry. There is a river nearby, it must be the Nile but there is no food. I can not get over what I have done. Tonight I am going to go back to the city to tell my family what I have done. I will also get some cattle and cloth.

7.35pm Now I have stopped right outside the city, I don't know if I should go in or not. I am going to go because I have to tell the truth to my family. First I will go to the palace then to the market.

8.00pm I have just told the family what I have done and been to the market. They're very angry now, I'm going home. Bye for now.

Kim Lawrence (11)
Ley Top Primary School

A Day In The Life Of A Wolf Spider

Morning came, the wolf spider came out of its nest and went hunting for food. Firstly it ran along the ground looking for prey. Secondly when it saw an object (insect) it stood still. Then it crept slowly towards its prey, like a cat stalking a mouse. Finally, with a burst of speed it charged towards the insect and bit it. The poison soon paralysed it and the spider ate it. Then it caught some more for its family. For the rest of the day the wolf spider made a web and caught a wasp, ten flies, a spider and a baby bird. Finally the spider wrapped up all its food and took it back to its nest and had a feast then slept for a long time. The wolf spider's Latin name is 'lycosidae' and lives in woodlands, gardens, deserts and grasslands. The average size of a wolf spider is approximately 4-34mm. These large spiders have long legs and big eyes. The wolf spider's long legs help them to run fast on land and even cross water. It has eight big eyes to see even behind them. Wolf spiders live near ponds. They run across the top of the water, grabbing insects that are drowning. Wolf spiders always hunt alone.

Joshua Thompson (10)
Ley Top Primary School

A Day In The Life Of My Dog

The first thing I would do is wake up and walk around the kitchen, Next, Paul and Dan would come in and play with me for a while. After I would play with my favourite toy before going into the kitchen for some breakfast.

Dan would then go off to school and Dass would get up. After that Dass would take me for a walk for about half an hour. When Paul and Dan get back from school, they give me some lunch and then I would play around the house and then go to bed.

Paul Sanderson (10)
Lindhead Primary School

A DAY IN THE LIFE OF HARRY POTTER

At 8.00am I woke up, I put on my glasses and looked around. I got up, stretched and changed into my robes. I woke up Ron (my best friend). At 8.15am me and Ron tried to find the breakfast hall, but we were found by Filch (the student hating caretaker) trying to get in the Forbidden Corridor. We finally found breakfast and ate quickly. At 9.00am we went to Charms, we were doing the cheering charm, both of us came out in hysterical laughter (as we both over did it).

At 10.00am we went to Potions, we both hated it because Snape is our least favourite teacher. I lost 50 points for not adding one ingredient! We came up from the dungeons and went to dinner (yum, yum trifle for desert). At 12.30pm, we walked down the grounds to Care of Magical Creatures. Hagrid was standing near his hut, 'Oh no, no the Blast Ended Skrewts!' I shouted.

I came out an hour later, burnt, stung and bruised. At 1.30pm I walked in Transfiguration. We were supposed to turn a beetle into a button. I just gave mine a lot of exercise. At 2.30pm I went to defence against dark arts. I couldn't fight the Boggart because Voldemont might come up. At 3.30pm I went to Quidditch practice (boring). At 7.30pm I went to bed. At 9.30pm I went for a midnight walk, using the invisible cloak and marauder's map, then I finally went to sleep.

Alfie Maroney-O'Brien (8)
Lindhead Primary School

A DAY IN THE LIFE OF A TIGER

6.30am. I was snoring my head off, I was having a bad dream, you could tell by the way I was talking in my sleep.

8.00am. I wake up, I was so hungry I went out straight after I woke up. I looked for breakfast, I could eat 12 hundred elephants, that would be delicious. I heard something, it smelt like a zebra, that's just come out of the bin. It was horrible, I looked, I was right but not about the bin part. I was about to jump but I thought it was a waste of energy. I looked for elephants. I was in luck. I pounce, I got him and he was juicy. I went to play with my friend called Zara, she's as pretty as me. I had to go home, when I got home, I asked mum if we could go for a walk and look for dinner. Mum said, 'I'm a bit hungry.' So we set off, we found some zebras, Mum pounced, so did I. He was hard but I managed, I went to have a look around, I found a lion cub, her name was Zanya, her dad was scary but not as scary as mine.

My dad's the king of big cats, I am a prince.

I went home for tea, it was deer. I played with Mum. She can be funny sometimes. She fell over about 10 times. I went to bed at 6.00pm and fell asleep.

Lauren Cooper (9)
Lindhead Primary School

A Day In The Life Of A Dog

In the morning, Gran comes and when she comes, it is fun because I nick her brushes when she tries to clean up, then I have some dog treats for my breakfast. Then Mum comes back from the supermarket and Mum says, 'Get out the way Spike.' I tried to jump over the gate but can't yet.

I am going to get my Spike bone and play with it. Then my next door neighbour came out to hang the washing out.

'Hello Spike,' Woof! Then the next door neighbour's dog came out and came over to the fence to say hello. Then my mum shouts 'Spike! Time for walkies!' I ran to my mum and she put me on my lead. We went across the park, up the hill and to the White Horse and back again. Then Andy came back and I played fetch with him.

Michael Barker (9)
Lindhead Primary School

A Day In The Life Of A Fairy

8.00am.

I woke up this morning and it is a Monday morning, I went down, then I went out to play for a bit. I was wearing a green top, a white gown and some blue shorts. I have brown hair, I have a mum but my dad is dead.

12.00pm.

I have a den in a hole, I go there when I'm sad, my name is Elsie and I am a fairy. I have a fairy house and lots of clothes.

12.00am.

It is 12.00am and I am in bed but I can't sleep because an owl is hooting and it will not stop.

4.00am.

It is early in the morning and I am having some toast and then I am going for a walk. I saw lots of cats and dogs eating on the streets and when I got back, I saw something in my garden. It was my mum.

Elise Stafford (10)
Lindhead Primary School

A Day In The Life Of A Wrestler

In the morning I got my champion belt and went to Smackdown Arena. I got there and William Regal said that I had a match against Kurt Angel for my title. I had my match. I was a little nervous. The bell rang and we started our match. I came in with a punch in the stomach and then the Spinebuster. I picked him up and kicked him and did the Stunner. I pinned him and I got a 2 count. I did an arm wrench and he reversed it and hit me. He kept on hurting me. I got out of the ring and got the table.

I put it in the ring and got on the top ropes with him and did the Superflex through the table and I pinned him and won.

I went backstage and Triple H hit me with a chair, and then the Pedigree. Then I got up and went to William Regal's office and I shouted at him because I wanted a match against Triple H. I got my match but then he said 'It's for your title!'

Then after another match, it was mine again, and I thrashed him to bits, he got put through the table and got hit but I won. Then the Undertaker and Kane came in and wanted the tag team title against me and The Rock so they got their match and played the game.

We started the game, me and The Undertaker started and we were kicking each other in. Then I did my Spinebuster and did the stunner and pinned them but he kicked out at two. I tagged The Rock and he did the rock bottom and the people's elbow and we won the tag team belt.

Martin O'Sullivan (9)
Lindhead Primary School

A DAY IN THE LIFE OF A PIRATE

I Rolling Roger woke up on my boat this morning and put my hand in the water and grabbed a fish. 'Yum, yum!' I had caught a fish for my parrot, Percy.

Then I tried to start the boat, it wouldn't start 'Oh no.' We will just have to row.

'To that island over there, my little bird, let's row, come on, come on.'

We got to the island, we saw a tower and it looked good. We got on the island and there were loads of fossils and under the fossils I found a treasure box.

'Take it back to the boat. Come on. Shall we go back to the boat for the night?'

Dan Kearney
Lindhead Primary School

A DAY IN THE LIFE OF MY DOG FLOSSIE

I sleep in the human's kitchen but when I wake up, all the humans come downstairs and give me a really good stroke. Then I have a nice stretch, I think to myself, that's a lot better, I walk into the dining room and I lie down next to the computer. After a while, a big tall human comes and ties a lead to me and I go for a nice long run through lots of fields. Just what I need in the morning.

I come home and lie in the back garden, then have a drink. It now becomes afternoon and a girl comes back from school, then feeds me. Mmmmmm she plays with me for a while but then the day ends. The humans all go to bed so do I. But . . . what's that, I hear the sound of breaking glass. Someone's there, I growl grrrr, I thought, I'm going to bite you but when I did, the sound was like an alarm. All I could hear was ouch. He soon ran off though and I went back to sleep. That's much better.

Bethany Gargan (9)
Lindhead Primary School

A Day In The Life Of My Pet Dog

I got up and felt to tired, so I went back to sleep.

I wake up again because my middle owner is going to take me for a walk.

We both get back from the walk. On the walk, I ran around and the middle human threw a stick for me. I go back to sleep.

Then after a while, the little human gets up (oh no), then middle human and little human walk out of the door, then the big human gets up and gets a shower and gets dressed and lets me out in the back garden.

I then come back in and I get my toast (Yummy) and as I am having my toast, the door slams because the big human has gone out the door. Now I'm left alone. I walk about the house waiting for the postman.

At last the postman has come, I start to bark at him.

Now I walk about the house (boring). At the same time, I guard the house then I play with my ball for a while.

Then I go to sleep and when I've had a sleep, little and middle human have come back. Little human plays with me, little human then turns on the TV, it's classical music (I howl to it).

The little human goes outside to play (it's not fair, I want to), the little human then comes back in.

Georgia Cain (9)
Lindhead Primary School

A Day In The Life Of A Fox

I woke up in my den this morning. I was very tired. I tried to get back to sleep but I couldn't. Vixen awoke a few minutes later. The fox cubs were awakening now too. I decided to go and look for some food for the fox cubs, Vixen and myself. I yawned and walked out of my den.

I didn't find much this morning, just a few scraps. The streets were silent. Everyone must have still been asleep. I went back to the den and gave everyone their fair share of food. For a while everyone just sat silently and ate. Then I said to Vixen, 'Why don't we go and explore? The cubs can stay deep in the den and finish their food.'

So the fox cubs hid deep in the den and Vixen and I went out to explore the streets. All of a sudden, when me and Vixen had gone a little away from our den, I heard loud, big trumpets and huge hounds barking madly. It was the fox hunters!

'Quickly Vixen,' I said, 'I will go one way and the hunters will follow me, you go home to the fox cubs. Be careful!' So I ran through a fence. Vixen went home, I could smell the hounds getting closer to me. I ran across some fields and jumped over a few stepping stones to cross a small river.

The hunters were still following me! I needed to hurry! I ran across another field, through some back gardens of our now noisy village, I went up some trees that hung over a stream. The fox hunters were still there!

I jumped towards the bank of the stream, I almost tumbled into the stream. Once I was on the bank I didn't bother looking behind, I just scurried up the bank and finally got home. Luckily the hunters decided to give up on me and go home. Safe at last!

For the rest of the day no hunters came. Me and my family stayed safely in our den apart from when I went to get our dinner. I had to work hard to get anything but I managed to get us all a delicious meal. I started to feel quite tired early in the evening tonight. I went to sleep when Vixen and the cubs did but I knew I would have the same sort of today, tomorrow, hunter's hunting us and probably another early night!

Kelly May (8)
Lindhead Primary School

A Day In The Life Of A Fox

It's getting night now, after the farmer has gone to bed. I will get a chicken and eat it. Running up to the farm, I got a chicken and I ripped its leg off, then its head, other leg and wings. That was nice, I liked its leg the best. Yes that was yummy, I like chicken the best. I think I've got an idea. I will play around with the chickens, I will run with them. Oh no, the farmer is coming with the shotgun, he nearly got me in the back. Yes, I got away from the farmer. I will not play with the chickens again.

I will have to go soon, it will be sunrise soon, but I will go to my friend's house to play with him. After a while, we play catch the chicken, I am trying to play something else but he wanted to play it so I played with him. But you can guess what happened, they shot my friend in the legs but he is resting, I think he will live. The sun is up now so I am going now, bye.

Edward Thompson (10)
Lindhead Primary School

A DAY IN THE LIFE OF A BLACKBIRD IN MY HEDGE

The sun comes up, the moon goes down, I slowly open my eyes. I feel the warmth of the chicks as they lay sleeping, sleeping. The time turns to 8.30am tick tock, tick tock. I sit watching for the white fresh bread to be laid on the wet green grass. The sound of footprints come walking along the garden path, walking, walking. I watch the bread being laid, I swoop down as fast as I can and start to fill my beak with bread. My chicks open their beaks and start to call me so I dive back into the hedge. Then I fly over the house and into the back garden. I started to dig for worms, dig, dig, dig, dig.

1.30pm eat the yummy worms,

2.30pm drift off to sleep until the next bright sunny day.

Bethany Sarchfield (10)
Lindhead Primary School

A Day In The Life Of A Viking

I get woken up and I get told that we have to go to war so I went to the blacksmith's for a new sword.

I go to war in the Viking boat, we get on to land and start the war and a lot of people are getting killed.

We win the war from the fight, sail back with just 20 people left.

Couldn't find my house but then I spotted it.

I live a normal life with all my friends and people in a big house.

James Sixsmith (10)
Lindhead Primary School

A Day In The Life Of An Owl

1.00am. I'm going to make a fluffy bed out of twigs, leaves and soft feathers.

1.30am. I am going to talk to the blackbird and sing a tune.

2.00am. Dive down into bushes taking care of looking for mice.

2.15am. Take the mice back to the oak tree where I live.

3.00am. I'm going to take a long nap after all that working.

4.00am. Wake up slowly not to wake any other animals up.

4.30am. Eat mice up one by one - mmmmmm!

5.00am. Play with birds, sing again, my beak is getting sleepy.

5.15am. Nasty human comes out (looking sleepy) pokes me with sticks, run back in.

5.30am. Fly to another tree to see my wife and see if eggs have hatched.

6.0oam. Go to sleep, huddled against my wife.

Aimee Scott (10)
Lindhead Primary School

A Day In The Life Of A Dog

8.00am. Matthew woke me up but I couldn't be bothered to get off my beanbag but I still had breakfast.

9.15am I went in the garden and I was chased by my mum.

12.00pm Mum locked me up while she went to school.

12.30pm I watch the washing go round and round and round and round.

1.00pm Mum came back, I was hungry but I never got any food.

2.00pm I played about in the garden.

3.00pm Matthew got back from school.

4.50pm Becky got back from school (They never play with me).

7.30pm Dad got back from work.

10.00pm Went for a walk.

10.30pm Go to sleep.

Matthew Shone (9)
Lindhead Primary School

A Day In The Life Of A Computer

Mrs Robinson came into the classroom and turned me on but I didn't want to come on, so I broke down. At playtime, this ugly man came into mend me. As soon as he had fixed me, Natalie came into the classroom to play on one of my games. (I made her loose). I am very ticklish and the mouse kept on tickling me. When she came off, I broke down again. I don't like it when people come and torture me! So, this ugly man came in again to mend me but I didn't let him. At lunchtime I was pretty hungry so I ate the disk that was in my mouth.

After the last lesson, another boy came on but I was broken so he came off, a few minutes later Mrs Robinson turned me off but I didn't want to go to sleep so I booted up again. Mrs Robinson got really mad and kicked me and believe me, it hurt. So I quickly went to sleep to get the pain away. In the morning, there was a big dent in me. I thought it would be there for ever and ever.

Lydia Jackson (9)
Lindhead Primary School

A Day In The Life Of A Hamster

Day: Monday
Weight: 5 ounces
Food: lost count

I went to the beach and had 10 ham sandwiches. I was in my cage trying to store my hamster food in my pouches. I went to my nice warm cosy bed.

Day: Tuesday
Weight: 8 ounces
Food: 5

I played in my wheel and got held by humans. I did some Olympics, did my teeth and went to bed.

Day: Wednesday
Weight: 1 ounce
Food: 11

Today is the day I tried to lose weight. I practised acrobatics in my cage, I also played in my ball and my wheel and I lost some weight.

Day: Thursday
Weight: 3 ounces
Food: 8

Today I couldn't help myself, humans were asleep and I'm fattening up. Today I ate lots of food and watched TV and films with my popcorn.

Day: Friday
Weight: 10 ounces
Food: 2

I danced when humans were having a party. Then it was my time to be awake. Then in the daytime I tried to get to sleep but the humans distracted me, they were still having a party.

Day: Saturday
Weight: 1 ounce
Food: 1

Today is the best day of my life. The humans went out to the pub and I had fun in my marvellous, excellent cage.

Natalie Culling (10)
Lindhead Primary School

A Day In The Life Of A Conker

'Ahh this is the life, growing in a tree,' Whack! 'Noooo I've fallen down the tree.' There's a human stomping on me and pealing all my skin off me and taking me out of my white bed. I'm going to faint.

When I woke up I had a big hole pierced through me and I was on a string. 'What's he doing now, he's covered me in glue, I've heard about this, some of my friends were put in an oven or soaked in vinegar.'

Ahhh! Playtime, the worst time of the day. Whack! He's just flung me onto another conker, ouch, he's giving me the worst headache ever. Dying, dying, dying, alert! Crack. I'm dead, what's he doing now, he's glued me back together, oh it didn't work. I'm well and truly dead. If there's people I like, it's the ones who plant me!

Tom Cappleman (9)
Lindhead Primary School

A DAY IN THE LIFE OF A SNAKE

8.00am. Slivering and sliming I get out of bed,

8.30am. It's ants for breakfast.

9.00am. I go and wake the babies up out of their deep, deep sleep.

9.30am. They don't get ants for breakfast, they get squashed up carrots instead.

10.00am. I go and play with the babies. We play hide and seek. They go and hide near a swamp, then they get eaten by hungry mean crocodiles.

10.30am. I go and have some lunch, it's a cow again but this time I don't have to share. Yum, yum, yum, yummy.

11.00am. I have a well deserved nap.

1.30pm. I bite and kill a juicy little lizard.

2.30pm. I have it for tea. Mmmmmm it's good.

4.00pm. I see a human walking past, I bite in yum, yum, yum,

5.00pm. I slip in my prickly damp bed in a ditch and go to sleep!

Charlotte Martin (9)
Lindhead Primary School

A Day In The Life Of A Panda

Aaaar I woke up and sniffed the fresh air.

'Oh no! My belly is rumbling again, that's right, time for breakfast.'

So off I went along the riverbank until I came to a patch of bamboo. 'Yum, yum,' I said munching on the bamboo sticks. When I had finished my tea, mummy said it was time for a nap but I started the silly cry again, so I ran off but I got myself into a bit or a lot of trouble. I say, it was my worst enemy, the tiger!

I was just about to climb quickly up the tree when he cut my leg, I was just so afraid to come down, just to get it off my mind, I had a little nap. When I woke up, it was time for dinner but I thought of my mum worrying a lot so instead of having my dinner, I went home. I got home at half past twelve at night but my mum was so happy that I was home, she cooked a big dinner to celebrate.

Amy Hirst (10)
Lindhead Primary School

A DAY IN THE LIFE OF?

The endless arguments, the screaming and shouting, the need to be far away, far, far, away. Monday morning, yet another Monday morning, the desperate urge to be dead.

Harry walked the dirt path heading for school. He looked a state, huge dark circles covered his usual glittering, blue eyes. His greyish shirt hung out of his short trousers but he didn't care, all he could think about was his parents' divorce. All he could see were the pictures of his parents fighting. That's why he didn't see the Ford Fiesta coming straight at him. That's why he's now lying in the middle of the road with smashed up glass surrounding him.

Suddenly, his eyes jumped open. Where was he? Instead of the broken glass around him there was white, misty smoke and he was no longer lying on tarmac but on something fluffy and bouncy. Ahead of him stood something or some one. They were wearing white robes, huge feather wings stuck out of them and something gold was floating above their head. Then it came to him, angels, clouds, he must be in Heaven, which meant he was dead. Slowly, he lifted himself to this feet. Harry's legs were trembling, his face moulded into a horrific expression, mouth open and eyes wide.

Abruptly the angel started to speak. She told him he wasn't in Heaven but in Deciders where you are given a task and judged on how well you do it, if you do it well you go to Heaven but if you don't you go to Hell. It was then a thought crossed his mind, what if I am a bad person? What if I go to Hell?

'What's my task?' he managed to blurt out through his dry and cracked throat. The angel answered with 'I don't know, we have to decide what would be good for you, I will let you know soon, for I am your guardian angel.' Quickly, the angel turned and left. Harry just stood there helplessly, what was he supposed to do now? Suddenly there was a tap on his shoulder, swerving around he saw the angel, in her hand was a notebook. She gave it to him. Harry tried to focus his eyes on the scrawny handwriting. On it, he read: Adia (guardian angel) underneath it said; task: you will have to be a marriage counsellor. Your main task will be to fix your parents' marriage. Signed, Judge of Deciders. Harry stared down at the notebook. How was he going to do this? Adia broke his gaze by asking when he would like to start.

'Now,' he blurted out, although he wasn't sure that was true. Before he could change his mind Adia tapped her halo three times.

At first Harry's eyes were blurred. When he could finally see again he saw he was sitting in an office, it had big leather chairs and was very neat. When he looked down, he saw he was wearing a suit and shiny shoes that were at least a size 10.

Harry had just finished admiring himself in the mirror when a woman entered the room, she had big hair and wore a pink suit.

'Your appointment with Mr and Mrs Weaver,' she said with a slight American accent. That's my parents, he thought, here goes!

Soon, his parents came in. Harry offered them a seat and tried to be natural. They started to talk about when they were first married and Harry jotted down notes. It didn't take him long before he realised that although they argued there was still a path to happiness through their problems.

The appointment soon ended and Harry said goodbye. Harry's thoughts wandered from his parents to Deciders. Where was Adia? What was he going to do?

Adia on the other hand was still in Deciders, stuck in a judging crisis. She too was worrying how she was going to get Harry back, but came to the conclusion to end judging and sent the problem man to Hell. Adia tapped her halo and whizzed to Earth to the office. She found Harry sitting on the leather chair deep in thought. He didn't notice her at first but quickly did. She told him he would sleep in Deciders tonight and the next appointment was tomorrow.

Harry lay awake that night thinking about the questions he would ask his parents the next day.

The bright sunshine shone onto Harry's face, he woke with a start. At first he didn't know where he was but soon became familiar with his surroundings again. Hurriedly, he put on his suit and went down to headquarters where he met Adia. Almost too quickly he found himself sitting on that leather chair facing his parents once again.

'Today could we talk about when your first child, Harry was born?' he quizzed. Although it wasn't obvious, Harry thought he could see tears in his mother's eyes. His parents started to explain how the arguments had started when Harry was born and how they were under a lot of stress so they took it out on each other. By the time they had finished talking, the hour was up. Harry's parents had left hopefully reconsidering their divorce.

The next day was Harry's final appointment, Adia had just come to wish him luck.

Dawn broke and Harry woke feeling more nervous than ever. He dressed and waited for his parents, they didn't take long. Harry noticed something different about them. They looked tired, as if they had been crying, then he realised they had only just heard about his death! Seconds later, this parents told him about it, broken-hearted, they talked and talked.

Harry suggested that now more than ever, they needed each other because each other is all they had. They actually believed him, his parents actually took him seriously! He had done it.

Harry's parents left and Adia turned up.

'Well done Harry! It's not definite but you are almost certainly going to Heaven, you still have to get past the judges but you probably will.'

At that point Harry had never felt happier through life or death.

Hannah Todd (11)
Naburn CE Primary School

MY HERO

If I had one wish, it would be to be like Kym from Hear'say because she really has a great singing voice. Ever since I was five, I have wanted to be a singer and I have never had a popstar hero until I watched Popstars.

I've sung in a pub in Boston because it was karaoke and I have sung at school talent shows but I really want to sing on TV. Me and my four best mates have made a band up called Glamour and our first song's called IV. I have been on TV when I was little but it was because the cameraman turned the camera to the audience and said
'Where's the mother of these two strangely dressed children?' and me and my sister had red matching dresses on. If I ever became a singer, I'll teach people how to sing.

I would do shows to raise a lot of money for charity.

I always sing in shops, supermarkets, even in class, but I really hope all this singing is worth it in a few year's time.

When we were watching a Britney Spears concert on Channel Five, she said
'If you believe you can do it, you'll go far,' and my grandma said 'Did you hear that Francesca? You might go far!'

I sang a song that I made up, to my teacher, Mr Browne and he said 'You've got a great talent.'

I really do hope I become a singer.

Francesca Brown (11)
Our Lady Of Perpetual Help Catholic Primary School

MY HERO ALAN SMITH

If I could be anyone in the world I wish I could be Alan Smith (a Leeds United player) because he is very talented and quite rich. If I was Alan Smith I would do the same thing as his team mate, Lucas Radebe. Lucas Radebe goes back to South Africa and gives some of his wages to his poor family and friends. I would also like to be like Alan Smith because he scores some really good goals against hard teams like Real Madrid, Deportivo La Coruña, Lazio and AC Milan. If I couldn't be him I would at least like to speak to him.

When I am older I would like a mansion and a really posh car but, of course, I will not be able to afford them both, but in the future Alan Smith will be able to afford it because he will be rich, so he will be able to afford it. That is another reason why I want to be Alan Smith. All of these reasons are about why I want to be Alan Smith.

Michael Hall (11)
Our Lady Of Perpetual Help Catholic Primary School

MY HERO

I was bored (as usual) then out of the blue appeared my hero, Michael Owen. He picked me up before I even had time to explain and ask him what he was doing here. But before I knew it I was standing in the middle of Wembley Stadium playing for England. All of the fans were screaming and I just sat there like an idiot.

'Come on Jade, we've got a game to win!' Michael shouted from defence. The white and red ball came closer to me and I started to imagine what would happen if I scored. 'Go Jade, get the ball!' She ran up and just kicked it slowly but with courage and it went in the fans go wild and she is a hero.

Then David Beckham came up to me and said 'Come on Jade, you can do it, just get the ball and go for it.'

'You're right!' I shouted to myself. I grabbed the ball and thought back to my imagination and I kicked it into the net. 'Yeah!' everyone shouted and then the final whistle blew and because of me England won Turkey 1-0! The fans were going wild and everyone was cheering for me. Then I suddenly ended up in my bedroom again and I heard Michael Owen say 'Well done!'

Jade Bates (11)
Our Lady Of Perpetual Help Catholic Primary School

DAISY

As soon as I opened my small, white petals the beautiful, inspiring feeling of life flowed through me like gushing water from a waterfall. From being cooped up all winter, I had to survive the bitter frost which killed lots of my fellow plants and I had to watch them die. Shivers ran down my stem as I tried to sleep, but the raging wind blew me this way and that, as I anchored my roots deep into the cold, wet and murky earth. But now all that has changed. Today I felt the soft, warm glow of the late spring sunshine, and I knew it was time.

As I stretched high, slowly but surely my petals bloomed like a mini fan and for the first time in nearly seven months I was happy. I was so happy, my golden heart glowed a bright yellow and my petal tips blushed pink. I swayed gently in the soft breeze, watching the insects and waving to my friends on the school field.

Suddenly the ground began to shake. Children the size of mountains stormed onto the grass, nearly squashing me. I trembled as I heard terrifying words, 'Daisy chain!' I buried close to the ground and prayed. Nearby I heard shrill screams, as stems were twisted and broken. I hoped it would be a quick death.

It was over. I had survived. Summer is fun, but dangerous for us. Enjoy it by all means, but please, we're living things too.

Helen Sullivan (11)
Our Lady Of Perpetual Help Catholic Primary School

MY DAY OF ALL DAYS!

Hello, I'm Shady Shark and I live in the Pacific Ocean and today I'm swapping places in life with someone called Robert Bedford. (Ever heard of him? Jolly nice person.) My swap starts right . . . now.

'Wehey, I'm a shark and I'm out for a kill because I'm hungry,' I said, so I set off to explore the Seven Seas and have an adventure. Soon I came to a coral reef and I saw a red fish and thought 'Yum!' So I chased after it and I eventually caught it and swallowed it whole. It was *flabbergasting!* It tasted gorgeous like pizza and ice cream mixed together. It sure did fill me up I'll tell you that for sure.

Next I went up to the surface to see what I could see, but all I could see was more sea - a bit of a tongue twister. I think I'll try scaring people next. So I went to the coastline and everybody ran out of the sea screaming out for help but I didn't plan to hurt anybody though. I just wanted a little fun that's all. Eventually everyone slowly came back into the sea and I left.

Soon I'd have to become human again but it was fun. Shady came back and we both told each other how great it was then we both turned to our normal selves.

Robert Bedford (10)
Our Lady Of Perpetual Help Catholic Primary School

BRITNEY SPEARS

I would really like to be a singer like Britney Spears and I wish I could meet her. Britney is the person I inspire the most.

My wish came true

On a hot summer's day I was playing out with my best friend Stephanie. I said to Stephanie 'I can't wait until my party next week because my mum has got a big surprise for me!'

Soon it was my birthday and I couldn't wait for the surprise. All my friends were there and we were waiting patiently. Then Britney Spears walked through the door and me and my friends were screaming. This was the best birthday party I ever had, I loved it.

Britney sang all of her songs and showed us some dances and taught us them. Then we had something to eat and I told her that I inspire her and I love her songs. When we had finished our meal we played some games and acted out some songs. Then Britney said 'You and your friends could come and watch me perform some time.'

I said 'Okay, that would be good.' Then we all shouted bye to Britney. We went back inside.

My mum said 'Did you enjoy that?'

I said 'Yes Mum and thank you.' Then all my friends went home and told their mums all about it.

Sophie Abbott (10)
Our Lady Of Perpetual Help Catholic Primary School

A Day Of A Snail

I came out of my shell and stretched my head. I felt a faint drop of water on my tail so I knew it was going to be a good day.

'It's raining!' shouted a slug. 'I can't believe it, it's the best day of my life. Yes, I will eat this leaf and that one, oh and this one.'

I knew who it was, Brad big mouth. He was always talking. 'Hello snail, I'm in a good mood today because it's raining.'

I started to slither on. Argh, a thrush. I quickly hid in a hole in the wall. It was trying to get in so it could eat me, but it got bored and flew away. I slowly slithered onto a tree and on a leaf. Well, it felt like a tree but it wasn't it was a nettle plant. 'Ohh my favourite,' I mumbled while I stuffed my face with nettle leaves.

Suddenly a little snail slithered up the stalk. 'Hello,' I said, 'have you come to eat yourself silly?'
'No,' the little snail told me. 'I've come to warn you, the dogs are coming.' Every week three big dogs come and trample down the stalk and vanish. I hoped for the best and slithered back home to a hole in a (real) tree. The dogs made the earth shake. Suddenly it stopped. I looked out of the hole, they had gone. What a snaily day I have had.

Stephanie Lewcock (11)
Our Lady Of Perpetual Help Catholic Primary School

MY HAMSTER HERO - SNUDGE

One day in Scawthorpe there lived a hamster called Snudge. He was a goldie coloured hamster and a very cute one too!

In Scawthorpe these past few weeks there have been a lot of burglaries. One night when we were in bed . . . *bang* went the burglar.

We ran downstairs very quickly (well me and my dad went downstairs first to check it out.)

A while later Mum came downstairs carrying my little sister, Sammy. She noticed that Snudge's bottle had come off his cage.

'Bethany!' she shouted. 'The bottle has come off Snudge's cage. Come and put it back on please.'
'Yes Mum, of course,' I said joyfully.

Mum put Sammy down out of her arms and walked into the kitchen. 'My rings,' she shouted. 'I took them off last night while I washed up. They meant loads to me.'

The next morning I made Mum, Dad and Sammy a cool drink to calm them all down and went outside to clean Snudge out. When I went back inside the house I noticed that mum was still upset and I knew something that would cheer her up. When I was cleaning out Snudge, in his house he had the rings. He must have got out of the cage and hidden them from the burglars. When I told Mum I felt happy for her. All the time now she strokes Snudge. She says that he is her *hero!*

Bethany Sarah Evans (11)
Our Lady Of Perpetual Help Catholic Primary School

A Day In The Life Of Dancing

I have always wanted to be a dancer, but I thought it would never come true until I met Charlotte Coverley. This is what happened.

I was walking down the street and there standing right in front of me was Charlotte Coverley, the world famous dancer. I went up to her and said 'Please can I have your autograph?'

She said 'Yes,' and I took her for tea at McDonald's. She had said she had enjoyed it very much. Then I thought it was time to ask her, 'Do you like being a dancer?'
'Not much, I wish I was a bit like you,' said Charlotte.
'I have always wanted to be a professional dancer ever since I was young and I thought we could swap places for the day,' I said.
'Wow, that will be great! Do you think we could?'
'I think so. Oh wow, this is great.'

So that is how I started. I will now tell you what happened when I was a dancer. Charlotte taught all the moves and what food I am supposed to like and what I had to do. It was very hard. At last it was time to go. I had to do seven shows and sign thousands of autographs.

At last the day was over. I was glad to be me again and so was Charlotte, but as I said, everyone should be happy with what they have and not want anything else.

Francesca Harding (11)
Our Lady Of Perpetual Help Catholic Primary School

MY HERO

It was the day before my birthday and I was about to go out for a disco in the Pavillion. The Pavillion is a huge white building in front of Future Park where every month the fair comes to make money.

When we got out of the door a very cool wind forced us to retreat back into the house. After fifteen minutes the weather wasn't getting any better so we decided to tell everyone it will have to be delayed even though we didn't want it to . When the weather finally got better it was too late to have a disco - it was half past ten, nobody was going to go to a disco at that time.

'It will have to wait till tomorrow,' said my auntie Deliah. She is a mean bean. She is always nasty to me when I go around to her house.

The next morning the weather was much better, the sun was out, we were on our way to the Pavillion - we were so excited. When we got around the corner we could see everyone waiting to get in. We opened the door and went in.

We were getting to the end of the disco when my mum said, 'We have a special surprise for you. Close you eyes.' So I did. 'Open your eyes now,' and there stood before me was my hero Eminem. I nearly fainted when I saw him, we stayed with him all night listening to his music.

Ian Davies (11)
Our Lady Of Perpetual Help Catholic Primary School

A CHEETAH'S LIFE

On one sunny day in Africa I was waking up in the cave which I live with my family. I have a mom and a twin sister. We're cheeky cheetahs, us two. As I woke my mom someone talked me, it was Nigel, my mate. 'Timber do you want to chase some antelopes?'

'I will be delighted to join you,' I replied, so we ran quickly as possible across the grassy meadow. We were there in no time cause we were fast runners. We ducked down and silently went down a steep hill.

'Let's go on three - 1 . . . 2 . . . 3!' shouted Nigel, then we pounced onto the antelopes as they panicked and rampaged on us.

'Where did they come from?'
'I don't want to find out,' shouted some of the antelopes. Then *bang!*

'What's that?' we asked each other. Nigel ran up the hill and saw poachers killing some lions then *bang!* 'Ohh!' roared Nigel then he rolled down the hill to me.

'No!' I screeched. 'I have to warn the others.' I ran really fast to the cave. At the cave everyone was angry after what I told them.

'Stand grand people,' said Jake, the leader of the pack.
'Poachers ahead!' shouted look-outs.

'Let's attack,' shouted everyone. A battle began. Many poachers and cheetahs died that day. I was one of them who survived. When night fell we saw packs of cheetahs. They took us in, then we were a family so were safe for now and always.

Kevin Pass (11)
Our Lady Of Perpetual Help Catholic Primary School

THE CHANGING TREE

In a wood a mile away from my house I found a little girl who had dropped her dolly inside a tree, I asked her what it looked like and got in the tree to find it. When I got in, there was no dolly there, I tried to get out but it was too deep. The next thing I knew a great big dog was standing there growling at me.

He was right in front of me, then he spoke, 'Who would you like to be for twenty-four hours.'
'I would like to be a dog.'
'You shall now be a dog,' he replied after a flash of light.
All I knew was that I was running around as a dog in the wood. I ran off out of the wood to find food. An hour later I was still looking for food. By this time I was really, really starving.

At last I found something to eat, an old sausage left by a human. I carried on walking through the damp streets. Twenty hours had gone by, I was dreading the last four hours. It was so boring until I saw an old ball. I started to play with the ball. After the four hours had passed I became certain I was changing back because I could see my fingers turning back to normal. When I was fully back to normal I returned home.

Claire Daly (11)
Our Lady Of Perpetual Help Catholic Primary School

NEIL ARMSTRONG

I would really like to be an astronaut like Neil Armstrong or 'Buzz' Aldrin because I really like science and space. I dream of taking people to a civilisation on Mars or another planet and exploring a new galaxy no one knows about. Finding aliens, white dwarfs and cures for diseases like cancer or meningitis or HIV and technology to shrink or enlarge cameras to discover what is wrong with people from the inside. Find a substance to replace fossil fuels and be harmless to the o-zone layer. Vehicles that can turn deserts into massive farming places and computers that can program robots with feelings. I want to prove aliens exist and walk on unknown planets.

Being an astronaut is my dream but I don't think I'll become one, but if I don't, I want to work for NASA or be an astronomer, or do something that involves space. I'm going to do lots of studying and go to college and university. I would probably faint if I got to be an astronaut, because I really want to be one.

Neil and 'Buzz' are two of my heroes and I want to be as brave as they were in space.

Paul Sullivan (11)
Our Lady Of Perpetual Help Catholic Primary School

MY HERO

It was a cold afternoon and I went downstairs to watch Top of the Pops then Robbie Williams came on.

God, I wish I was famous and everyone knew the words to my song. But I'll never be famous, though I can sing. I'm quite good but nobody ever listens and dreams don't come true.
'Of course they do!'
'Who said that?'
'I did!'

Suddenly the TV flashed and Robbie Williams came out of the telly.
'Look kid when I started I wasn't very good, then I joined Take That. It went really well then we split up and I fell to the bottom but I kept my hopes and dreams and released 'Angels' and that made me, and when 'Rock DJ' came out I was huge.'
'But how will I make it into the top ten?'
'Look when you get older sing at clubs, act in plays, get yourself heard!'
'Thanks!'
'Have you got any Pepsi?'
'Yeah, in the fridge!'
'Ta!'
'Will you sing for me and some of my friends?'
'OK!'
I walked to the phone and phoned up Michaela.
'Michaela, guess what, Robbie Williams is at my house and is going to sing, come round as soon as you can!'
'I'll be round in an hour!'
'Robbie, you're my hero!'

Charlotte Scott (11)
Our Lady Of Perpetual Help Catholic Primary School

I FINALLY MEET MY HERO

'EastEnders' one and only Jamie has organised for one lucky competition winner to spend a full day with him and then a meal at a snazzy restaurant to finish.' I overheard two teenage girls fantasising to each other.

I needed to know more, so at that moment I ran home as fast as lightning, I burst through the front door and collapsed in front of the TV. I picked up the remote and turned on the teletext. It took me a while to find the right page but it finally popped up. They wanted girls to write a 1000 word essay about their dream date including the person you want the date with.

I started straight away, it needed to be good if I wanted to win. Three hours passed and there must have been more than 50 scrunched up pieces of paper covering my bedroom floor. This is going to be the winning entry, I kept saying to myself. Five hours passed and I was on my final word. I rushed out hoping to catch the last post.

A week passed until I heard a beep outside. I ran out where a limo was parked. 'It couldn't be,' I screamed.

Jamie got out and I went weak at the knees. I jumped into the car where Jamie said, 'We are going to a new theme park.'

When we arrived Jamie had a phone call, 'Sorry, I have to go!' he groaned. He kissed me on the cheek and gave me some cash for a taxi. 'My hero,' I sighed.

Sinead Epton (11)
Our Lady Of Perpetual Help Catholic Primary School

A DAY BEING A FARMER'S WIFE

I've been stuck here for weeks, months, no one can get in, no one can get out. My cupboards are empty but more to the point my husband's farm is deserted in the heart of Devon. I wake up every morning to the musty burning smell of animal flesh. My supplies of home-made bread and jam have run dry. That familiar buzz is just not here anymore. My once busy days have just drifted away.

My children have gone away to live with their grandparents up in Yorkshire where it is not as badly affected. I thought I would save them the pain of letting them see their pet lambs 'Woolly' and 'Fluffy' smouldering on a heap with others. At least their ponies are safe from the devastating outbreak of foot and mouth disease.

Eggs it is again for lunch, good job we have chickens! My weary husband has just stumbled through the door, blood stains everywhere. Usually by this time he is bringing in newborn lambs to warm by the Aga, but all he is bringing in is the smell of death.

My only consolation is that everywhere is spotless. I can only look forward again to the days when we have lambs gambolling in the fields with the spring grass is green instead of brown charred patches we look out upon. The smell of daffodils and warm April rain and I can once again nurture my living stock.

Lucinda Ashworth (12)
Queen Mary's School

A Day In The Life Of A Fox

I slowly opened my sleepy eyes as the first rays of sunlight hit my earth cavern. I sniffed the air and could smell the faint whiff of a scrumptious rabbit, but I had to wait until night to do my hunting. I could already taste the warm, wet blood soaking my tongue. I suddenly heard the sound of horses. They were just outside my earth, but I could relax, they were only trotting by with their owners. I decided to have a snooze, for there was to be an exciting and appetising night ahead.

I woke up feeling very hungry. The darkness crept in like a curtain. A wave of cold air swept through my fur, but I didn't notice, for there were rabbits to eat and chickens to kill. I crept along the damp ground and smelt the horses that came by earlier. However, there was another smell that stung the end of my nose. It was rabbit. I followed the scent with my nose to the ground as it got stronger and tastier. I dug at what I knew was the rabbit's burrow. I stuck my leg down the hole and felt a rabbit streak past my paw. With my quick reactions I managed to snatch its hind leg and quickly brought it up into the open before it could get away. I dragged it back to my warm cosy earth and tore it open ravenously, eager to fill my hungry stomach.

Anna Coles (11)
Queen Mary's School

A DAY IN THE LIFE OF AN URBAN FOX

One summer's evening, whilst it was still light, I decided to go hunting for our night meal. However, as I left the cubs sleeping quietly in the den and crossed the road behind our dustbins, I felt a violent roaring and rumbling shake the ground. I heard a loud blaring horn and I looked up to see two dazzling white lights thundering down the road towards me. I was paralysed with fear, but I managed to roll safely out of the way just as the car raced past.

Once I had recovered from the shock, I met another danger. Lying at the side of the pavement was a fat, juicy hedgehog, its legs stuck up in the air. Just in time however, I noticed the sinister trail of electric-blue slug pellets leading away from the poisoned hedgehog. I shuddered as I thought of how close I was to being poisoned myself.

Minutes later I was on the trail of a rat. I had smelt it when I was exploring the park on the other side of the road. I saw its tail slithering round one corner of a dusty red brick house and soon I was ready to attack it.

Suddenly, I heard a whimpering howl and the rat turned, saw me and scampered away. Cursing the creature that scared my prey, I turned for home.

As I entered the den, I had another shock. There on the floor was a dead vole! The cubs had found our evening meal!

Alistair Pickup (11)
St Chad's Primary School, Leeds

A Day In The Life Of A Great White Shark

Do you know what I did today? No you don't do you? I killed two scrumptious little children. One was very fat and podgy, I think he was a male. I killed another one, one of the other kind, umm, let me think. Ah yes, it was a female, she was quite meaty too. The rest of my family came and gobbled up the rest of them. I also chased a dolphin, but sadly it escaped my bloodthirsty jaws.

Later in the day I found a family of seals bathing in the water. I waited until some of the youngest and weakest and most helpless of them all came without protection, and crunch, my sharp jaws enclosed on their moist succulent, meaty bodies.

After that I decided that I would scare a few females water skiing. I like chasing them because they scream and it is fun making them scared. A shark fishing boat came after me, when I was chasing the girls. I was really scared. Fortunately I managed to get underneath the fishing boat and bit a huge chunk out of the bottom. I managed to kill the shark fishermen so they couldn't go after any other sharks like me.

Some people came to watch me in my natural habitat. They threw a chunk of fish out, but I didn't take it.

Remember to look out for me when you are snorkelling or diving or I might, if you don't get away, eat you!

Elspeth Kirkham (11)
St Chad's Primary School, Leeds

A Day In The Life Of A Mouse Called Minnie

I was minding my own business, just having a stroll about the kitchen, looking for bits of cheese when big hairball, Fluffy the cat, came round the corner. I scuttled into the hole underneath the cupboards hoping he wouldn't see me. But he went and did it again! He spotted my tail just as it was disappearing into the hole to join me. I made a run for it. I circled the table a few times and pretended to go into the living room but instead, raced under the gap of the downstairs toilet door. Phew, I was away! I closed my eyes to rest and the next thing I knew, I was being woken up by the creek of the toilet door as Ben came in. I dashed out through the door then through the cat flap, but only to find Fluffy and three of his cat friends miaowing to each other. I crept slowly towards the car but the four cats pounced from the wall and started to chase me. I decided to head for the park just around the corner. By this time the cats were gaining so I rocketed through the park gates and did as many laps round the pond as I could manage. I was just about out of breath when two cats came from one side and two from the other. They all hit heads like stones and were out cold. That was my ticket to get out of there, go home and rest.

Lee Debenham (11)
St Chad's Primary School, Leeds

A DAY IN THE LIFE OF A NEWS REPORTER

As I awoke from my sleep I heard the phone ring slowly. I walked across the room to answer it. As soon as I had heard it all I suddenly became really excited. I found myself at the office with no time to spare. It was 6am, when my manager came over to me, I was getting nervous, all I could think about was what I had to do.

When I heard what I had to do I didn't know what to say. Mt Versuvius in Pompeii had erupted and I had to go and do a report on it. The plane landed in Rome because there was no airport in Pompeii. I received a hire car so I could get to Pompeii. As I passed the sad looking faces of the survivors I could see that it had been terrible. I set up the cameras and interviewed a few people. All of them said the same thing, 'It just erupted.'
As the news started there was a shake from the ground. Suddenly, hot molten lava burst out of Mt Versuvius, I didn't know what to do so I ran. I ran as fast as I could to the car and drove off with the hot lava on my trail, but slowly it died away and I returned home safely.

Joshua Lowcock (10)
St Chad's Primary School, Leeds

A DAY IN THE LIFE OF A PUPPY

Hi! My name is Scuffy. I live at number 29, Kennel Street. I am a grey puppy with, well, at the moment, a lot of mud stains all over me. Oh! That's my owner shouting me. Is it dinner time already? Goody! I'm starving!

This is my home. What? Whoa! Oof! Oooops! I spilled my water. Yummy! Chicken and gravy. My favourite! I'm vewy hungwy. Buuurrrp! Sorry about talking with my mouth full. Now then, where's my water? Oh, right I spilled it. My owner is bringing some more. Gulp, gulp, glug, glug. Ahh. Oh no! I need to get outside! Nearly there! Oooopppsss! I *almost* made it. Hey, what do you think you are doing? Well, how do you like that? I've just been plonked outside and left here. It's not my fault I couldn't get outside fast enough. I'm just going to have to look for my bone. I think I left it here, right by the petunias, or was it the poppies. Maybe the pond? I am digging and a flower flies through the air straight and lands on my head. Maybe it's not in here after all. Next I will try the pond. Aaaarrrggghhh! Splash! Oh bother. I shake myself and trudge back to my kennel. Oh! Here's my bone. I will go to sleep now. Goodnight.

Sandra Rosie (11)
St Chad's Primary School, Leeds

A Day In The Life Of A Cat

Hi, my name's Billy. I live at 16 St Chad's Rise and I have five wonderful owners called Laura, Hannah, Alex, Carole and Stuart. I'm white, ginger and grey.

I woke up one morning with a present waiting for me. A gold collar with a bell on it and a name disc with the inscription 'Billy' on it. My breakfast was prepared, poached salmon and fresh cream. It was like being in a hotel! I was so lucky! I decided I was going to make this the best day of my owners' lives.

It was a warm summer's day and the sun's rays were beaming down on me. I went to the woods to try and spot a present for my owners. There were lots of birds, mice, leaves and children playing. There were lots of noises like birds singing and leaves rustling by the gentle breeze.

I saw a mouse out of the corner of my eye and one swipe of my paw was enough to catch it!

I returned home with the 'prize' mouse. It was grey, with white ears, pink eyes and very, very long whiskers. Just the type I normally like to eat actually! I left it by the front door, dead of course! Ready for my owners when they come back from school and work. I was so pleased with the present I had chosen I thought to myself, 'I know they'll like this present!'

Hannah McLean (10)
St Chad's Primary School, Leeds

A DAY IN THE LIFE OF A COUNTRY FOX

I love chasing chickens! I've even made a game of it. How many I can catch in thirty seconds! Tonight I caught two plump ones. They should last!

I dragged them out of the dusty barn and ran for my life before that skinny farmer could shoot me. At my den, my cubs seemed pleased with my find as they just couldn't wait to dig in!

After the chicken had been turned into a rug, the meat was eaten and the bones were scraps, I decided to find another one, just for me. I creeped, stealthily out into the dawn, trotted along a dirty path and sprinted towards the farm. But then I stopped on the spot, my ears twitched, and I heard the terrible sound of horses galloping towards me! They were accompanied by twenty dogs, barking, growling, chasing. But there was no time to think, I just zoomed away.

But still, they were gaining on me. I had to think fast - where was the safest place I knew of? Then it hit me, my den! How obvious! One of those raging dogs nearly bit my tail off. I was really angry now.

I ran into a cluster of trees where I knew a shortcut to my den. I had lost the horsemen now because I could hear them cursing. I dived through the undergrowth and into my den, where my cubs waited.

Thomas Walker (11)
St Chad's Primary School, Leeds

A DAY IN THE LIFE OF A TALL OAK TREE

As I stood peering into the large building site I gazed into the quiet school yard in semi darkness. The dawn broke. I saw people move in the shadows and I saw many cars go swiftly by. As the light shone down in full force, builders and school children started to arrive. I saw a tall, dark man opening the large school gates and the children began flooding in. I spotted a queue of cars building up, the noise was deafening with all the horns honking. As the queue disappeared I spotted the children coming out. A group of girls started skipping. I saw one boy push another and then run away. I stared hard at the tall lady coming out of the building. She rang a large bell and led the children inside. I swayed gently and then jumped as a loud sound came from the building site, it was a tractor starting up.

Children came out and started having PE, some were skipping while others were running. The children soon went inside and then suddenly the nest in my branches with the chicks in began to tweet wildly. The workers soon stopped and disappeared while the children I saw came out again. I stood for ages doing nothing; the workers seemed to have stopped altogether. I peered round and noticed the rush hour seemed to have started along with the children going home. Larger children came along and started pulling off my lower branches, it hurt. As I sat there feeling upset, I hadn't noticed when the darkness came over and I was left in the well lit street.

Tifaine Baskerville (11)
St Chad's Primary School, Leeds

A Day In The Short Life Of A Microbe

One morning, a tiny microbe was born in a river. As it came out it was swept for miles and miles (kilometres in metric) until it was in an unfamiliar pool. It has a brilliant time exploring until it came to a caterpillar's lair. The caterpillar looked very hungry and a high speed chase began through a cave. The speed of the caterpillar was almost the same as the speed of the microbe. The microbe was absolutely terrified. Suddenly a huge rock dropped from the roof of the cave. It just gave the microbe time to escape. The light outside was amazing compared to where it had been.

The microbe had a quick snack before doing a bit of leisurely swimming. Instantly it found an underwater cave that it had seen. The microbe was so curious that it had to go inside. Soon after he wished he hadn't hundreds of angry ninja bacteria were waiting inside.

The microbe was glad it knew how to swim. Only 5 ninjas chased it but they were extremely fast. Yet again, the microbe was terrified. It ran a swerving course, with 3 crashing straight into rocks! All of them were killed.

Suddenly the remaining two stopped chasing. 'I wonder why?' thought the microbe. It never knew. The microbe had swum into the caterpillar's lair. The caterpillar slew the microbe with a terrible blow. That is the end of a microbe's short day.

Graham Andrews (10)
St James' CE Primary School, Wetherby

A Day In The Life Of Robbie Burrows

05.30
My alarm goes off, I get out of bed with a struggle, I have to be at Headingly for o7.30, a hard day of training is about to come my way.

06.30
I put my kit into the bag and heave it into the car. I'm still half asleep but I must do lots of training to prepare for the match tonight.

07.35
Finally, I arrived at Headingly, Darrell blows my head off for being late, he tells us the match will be easy and that Huddersfield Giants are rubbish. I don't know, I have never played them.

14.15
Have not stopped all day. I'm sweating like mad. The match is drawing closer and for once I am nervous. The cheerleaders are practising their dance routines, our mascot is working on his backflips and as for us, the players, we're exhausted.

18.40
We have been training all day up until now. Darrell has given us an hour break to do what we want as long as we are back to change into our proper kit. Kick off is at eight. I have seemed to calm down, but I am still not looking forward to this match.

20.00
The match is about to start, the Huddersfield players are jogging onto the field, my legs are shaking and my palms are sweating, I won't be able to write in here for forty minutes.

20.30
We are playing all right, we are winning and I am very sweaty and dirty, better go, match is starting up again, wish me luck!

21.30
We won, we played pretty rubbish compared to our normal standards, I'm drained and I'm going for a well earned beer.

Becki Suttle (11)
St James' CE Primary School, Wetherby

A DAY IN THE LIFE OF KATHERINE LAVENDER
(Rap)

Monday is a really big bore,
Mum is banging on the door.
Today we've got writing and spelling,
In the playground we do lots of yelling.
I need my spellin' book
And put my towel on the hook.
I put my pants and socks on,
Oh no, we've got Mr Don!
I put my skirt and top on,
I've got to get a new top
Because this is covered in muck.
Oh no! Look at my luck,
Ellie and Alice are annoyed
Because their toy's destroyed.
I have eggs boiled,
I don't like them spoiled.
Mum drives me to school,
Meet my friends, that is cool!

Danielle Beaumont (10)
St James' CE Primary School, Wetherby

A DAY IN THE LIFE OF A SCHOOL BOOK

Scribble! Scribble! Scribble! That's all you people do. And I have to suffer from it. You do not know how embarrassing it is for a school book to have an owner that has very untidy handwriting. You people give us school books no respect! No respect at all!

Oh and here he comes again! Opens me up clumsily then begins to shake his tacky fountain pen vigorously causing all these blots and marks all over my beautiful pages!

Oh and presses so hard it looks like he's been writing on the last page the exact same thing.

Oh! Kids these days. Never bother to do a spot of handwriting. Oh no! Too busy watching TV and playing on their nasty little Gameboys.
'Calling me tacky?'
Oh no! It's that *tacky* fountain pen. Oh it really gets on my nerves, it does, jabbering away like an old granny.
'And yes! I can hear you saying I'm a moody old killjoy.'
Honestly those pencils and rubber, they're as gossipy as some of you humans! And the work kids do these days as well. No marvellous and wonderful poems that will be world famous in the future. And those new school books, better not pick on me too. This lad hardly does any work. So trust me, I've been around and I know what's happening!
'See, I've worked hard for that silly little boy.'
'Broken record!'
'Oh the nerve of that pencil! I don't care if you think I'm a moody old killjoy. So *goodbye*!'

Sherin Bhasker (9)
St Joseph's Catholic Primary School, Dewsbury

A Day In The Life Of A Pair Of Trainers

Life begins on a shelf in the warehouse. I sneak up and look to see if it's us going, finally we've gone, yippee!

'Look we're being put on, that hurt, oh look, he's took us off, oho, we're going back to storage again, yippee!'

'Oho, someone wants us again, let's get ready, oh he's changed his mind, let's go back.'

'Yes, he's changed his mind again, we're going, look we have gone past the check out. Look out, a football, I'm dirty.'

'Aha, oh no, me too, we're going inside, he's took us off his feet, smell poo.'

'I'm glad he took us, his feet pong.'

'We're being washed, yippee, he's taking us to a party, he's playing football again, he's only just cleaned us.'

'Let's make him run back to his house and tell him not to get us dirty till we're six months old.'

'He's a messy boy, he spilt spaghetti on me Left.'

'I know Right, it splattered on me Right.'

His mum has told him off, aha. He's just dumped us, his mum has hung us up.

'I'm dizzy, are you Left?'

'Yes I am Right, I'm getting used to this now Right.'

'Me to, goodnight Left.'

'Goodnight Right.'

Esmond Howes (9)
St Joseph's Catholic Primary School, Dewsbury

A Day In The Life Of My Teddy Bear

This morning Molly put me on her toy box and went downstairs. When she went to school with her mum all the toys woke up and had a big stretch. Me and the rag doll played doctors with Mr Fox. Mr Fox has a soft fur coat and a pipe. The rag doll is knitted. She wears a pink dress with white tights. I have a fur coat which is very warm and a check bow tie.

Mr Fox was the doctor. We played doctors until 3.30pm, that's when Molly came home. We had to be very still. Molly's put me into her bag. I wondered where we were going. Bye rag doll, bye Mr Fox. Molly closed the bag, and off we went.

Later on Molly took me out of her bag. We were in the park for a teddy bear's picnic. Molly and her friends sat in a circle, there were lots of other teddies. I said hello to them. We all ate sandwiches and buns. Afterwards we went to the river, a naughty dog bit another teddy bear.

We went on a boat across the river. The mums and dads walked along the bridge. Molly nearly dropped me in the river but luckily she caught me. When we got to the other side Molly put me with the other teddies and went to play.

Later on Molly's mum said 'It's time to go home.'
'OK,' said Molly, 'let me get teddy.' Molly came for me. It was fun telling my friends about my day.

Alexandra Tolley (9)
St Joseph's Catholic Primary School, Dewsbury

A DAY IN THE LIFE OF A £10 NOTE

First I got stamped to a piece of paper and came out with little pictures all over me. They didn't look bad, but a bit older and with dull colours.

I got passed through to a long car in a big suitcase with loads of others of my kind. The car halted at a big store with dozens of food, household things and useful objects in little boxes.

The next thing I know I'm in a till full of money, in the pitch-black, when a man in a uniform picked me up and gave me to another person.

'Thanks,' the man said.
'Come again,' the shopkeeper replied.

This other man took me to a place called the 'Co-op Late Shop' and handed me to another man but in a different uniform. This happened over and over again.

This is pretty much my life . . . what's your life?

Lewis Kilroy (10)
St Joseph's Catholic Primary School, Dewsbury

A Day In The Life OF A Pencil

Jammed in a pencil case, no room to move or breath. I want to get out but I can't. I have a blunt lead, that is why I never get chosen.

Look, here comes Miss. Oh no! She's taking me to the bin. She puts me to a sharp blade, it scraps my skin off. At least now I have a sharp lead. Miss hands me to a girl. She presses me to the paper, scraps me to and fro, back and forward until I have a blunt lead again. She takes me to the bin and scraps me again, and then chucks me on the desk.

Now I can rest, I feel useful but why didn't I get picked in the first place? I have a shiny, silver pattern and a rubber on the end, but all the dull red ones always get picked because they all have sharp leads. I thought that my blunt lead made me unattractive along with me being short from the times I've been sharpened.

I've been picked up again and scraped over and over and over again until the end of the day. I'm put back in the case. So maybe it wasn't me, maybe the human couldn't be bothered to sharpen me.

Maria Preston (9)
St Joseph's Catholic Primary School, Dewsbury

A Day In The Life Of Elsa The Cat

Hello, my name is Elsa and I am an eleven year old cat. This is how I usually spend my day. My owner Hannah gets up and gives me my breakfast which I eat up right away.

After eating I go out and play in the sun. I play with my friends, Crunchie and Specs. We climb trees, chase birds and run around in the fields. This makes me a little tired so I like to get my head down for a while on the back wall.

Soon it is dinner time and I am running in for some biscuits and milk, then it is back outside for more fun with my mates.

Teatime comes and Hannah is home from school to give me my meal, which is a nice plate of cat food, my favourite is chicken.

When I have had my tea I nip into the room and lay in front of the fire while I give myself a good clean up. I am usually nodding off when Hannah picks me up and wants to play. Sometimes this can be annoying because I'm comfortable but I usually don't mind because I love her.

Bedtime comes and everyone has gone upstairs so I creep up the stairs and sneak into Hannah's bedroom and climb on her bed and go to sleep. This is the end of my perfect day.

Hannah Lawton (9)
St Joseph's Catholic Primary School, Dewsbury

A DAY IN THE LIFE OF A CHELSEA FAN

I've been entering goal of the month on 'Match of the Day' all season but haven't won a prize yet. The winner usually gets a trip to a match of their choice and takes a friend with them.

I entered again last month because I wanted to go to a cup final. Mum let me stay up to watch the programme but as usual I fell asleep on the settee. The next thing I knew mum was shaking me about saying 'You've won Paul, you've got tickets to the Chelsea v Ipswich cup game.'

I was on my way to Anfield, which was a neutral venue for this exciting game. I've hardly dared believe it's happening. Jamie, my brother, was coming with me. The crowds were building as we found our way to our seats in the stand. What a noise! All the Chelsea fans were chanting and I joined in. It was great to be in the middle of them. The whistle blew and the game was fast and exciting.

Chelsea made some early breaks but the Ipswich defence saw the challenges off . Ipswich had a shot but the goalie tipped it off the line. Half-time came with no score and while we waited for the second half we ate sausage rolls and drank Coke.

The teams came out and Ipswich kicked off and with some great moves scored an early goal. As they celebrated the goal the Chelsea fans started chanting 'Come on you Blues' and urged on the attack. By the end of the game Chelsea had pulled back and went one ahead with two stunning goals from Hasselbank, their top scorer. What a game! Chelsea lifted the cup and I celebrated with the crowd. I slept all the way home dreaming of my prize.

What a day out to see my favourite team Chelsea win the cup final.

Paul Taylor (9)
St Peter's Catholic Primary School, Doncaster

A DAY IN THE LIFE OF SADIE

I'm Sadie the dog and I live with my owners Janice and Sammy. I am sort of warm because it is in the evening. I love to play in the living room and that's where I am now. In the living room there are white pull-overs on the chairs, so I can never jump on them.

I wander off into the bedroom which is upstairs. I jump onto the bed and look out of the window. I can hear sirens. Suddenly I can see a fire engine driving towards an old building - it must be on fire. I hurry downstairs and start to bark. Janice and Sammy won't listen to me, as usual they are slouching on the settee watching TV. That's Janice and Sammy for you!

I jump up to the door handle and open the door, sprint outside and down the road. I followed the engine taking a short-cut across the field. The fire engine stops and loads of firemen hop out with a long weird thing. They turn it on and a load of water comes shooting onto the steaming building. It doesn't seem to be doing any good so . . . I run up to the building. I jump into a large gap, my eyes sting and my throat feels dry. I hear cries for help so I dash up some creaking stairs - they are very wobbly. I come to a maze, there are lots of corridors. I decide to go left , the cries are louder, I must be going the right way. I come to a door with a hole in it. I peer through it and see a group of people crowding round a small table. They are ducking down. I try to bark but I end up howling. The people all look up and shout to me 'The door is locked, go fetch help.' I can't see well so I look up and there is a key. I start to jump up and down, the key falls off, Yes, got it! I push it under the door. They all dive for the key. A young girl, who is coughing, shoves the key in the lock of the door and it flings open. The smoke seems to be going away, sort of being sucked.

All the people cheer as they get outside and see photographers who take photos of them and me, their hero.

The next day I look in Janice's paper. On the front page there is *me*, the super hero. Janice came in the room, they tell me well done and give me a plate of jumbo yummies, my favourite.

Siân Walker (9)
St Peter's Catholic Primary School, Doncaster

A Day In The Life Of A Tiger

Bang! A gun shot. It just missed me. I ran away as fast as a cheetah across to my hiding place where I was safe from severe danger. Phew, that was so close from my life being thrown away into nothing but death. I lay patiently waiting for the hunters to leave me in peace.

After that was done I went to find my prey. I felt the thick grass strimming past me as I crept as quietly as a mouse through the deep jungle. At last I saw my breakfast. At first I came up to the tree and stood silently behind my prey, a deer. Suddenly I leapt on it and it was lying dead. I gobbled it up like a snake putting its tongue back in his mouth. It tasted so scrumptious and yummy. I felt quite tired so I had a rest. I was about to fall asleep when I sensed a strange and very unfamiliar smell, which was quite subtle at first but then it got stronger. It was fire!

I ran and ran but soon it came racing up towards me, nearly burning my tail off. I roared in fright, still running faster and faster extremely close to losing my breath and dying. It was so noisy I couldn't take it. Luckily I found a little hole and I just jumped crazily in. After a while I fell asleep. I've survived for another day.

Anna Reilly (9)
St Peter's Catholic Primary School, Doncaster

A Day In The Life Of Me

My hamster is called Jessie. Jessie is right now playing football with my bouncy ball. He always plays with it.

'Come on Jessie, time for dinner. Mum, there is not any food for the hamster.'
'Well go and get some then.'
'But I need some money.'
'Well get some money then.'
'Okay, bye.'
'Bye-bye darling. Come back with some change.'
'Okay, bye.'

'Hi, I'm back.'
'Oh no, not Miss.'
'I am going to give Jessie some food.'
'Hi Jessie, I have got you some food. There you go, you can have some.'

My hamster is saying I am too full. I want to play. I wish I was here. I am back but I was asleep in her bed. I crawled out of my car. 'Oh no, I cannot play with him Mum.'
'You would not be able to play with him anyway because you are going to bed.'
'Okay, night, night.'
'Night, night darling.'
'Night Mum.'

Morning Mum.'
'Morning darling. Come on, you are going to be late for school.
'Okay, bye Mum.'
'Bye Jessie.'

Nicola Scrimshaw (9)
Sacred Heart School

A Day In The Life Of A Teacher

I woke up in the morning dreading the day ahead. I didn't mark the books last night, I couldn't think, I had no might. I walked into the class, what a bomb site it was.

Gary Stamps knocked over the bin. I shout across the classroom to this silly pest. 'You shouldn't have done that. You've got yourself a spelling test. Gary Stamps get over here, get that pencil our of your ear. Sarah, stop talking. Ross you think you are the boss. Kerrie go get a book and have a look please, you deserve a sweet.

'I have horrible feet,' says Georgina as she writes a poem.

Sarah does her hair and she reads on about a bear. I mark the register, everyone is here. I get pay today, I say. Gary sits at his desk, he is no longer a pest. Sarah is the pest, she is being silly. We sit on the carpet and read the book. I have a little sneaky look. We read the book, it is funny. My favourite animal is a bunny.

Katie Helliwell (10)
Sacred Heart School

A Day In The Life Of Gary Lineker

I was very tired. I didn't get to bed till 1 o'clock. I was going to Elland Road to watch Leeds verses Leicester with Alan Hanson. Mark Lawrenson was still celebrating Preston's win in the semi-final.

I got dressed and at nine o'clock I had breakfast. I looked in the mirror. My ears were sticking out. It reminded me of Nick Hancock taking the mickey, but it doesn't bother me, it's only natural. In no time it was quarter past one. Alan Hanson was picking me up at half past, I better get ready soon. Alan parped his horn, I got in and we were off. I was equipped with my Leicester shirt and my other lucky charms but they didn't work as we lost 3-1.

I got home and prepared for the last Match of the Day (until we buy it back off ITV - I live in hope!) In no time it was 8 o'clock, I was running late but I got to the studios on time. I was presenting MOTD with my two pundits, Alan and Mark. It was fairly emotional for all of us but we thought it would be back on BBC before long. We had a few jokes in amongst and we enjoyed it. It finished with the words 'See you after the break!'

Just another day at the office for a football crazy presenter I thought as I ate my salt and Lineker . . . I mean vinegar crisps.

Dominic Finn (10)
Sacred Heart School

A Day In The Life Of Maggie Simpson

At 4.00am I wake up, Marg is baking. I pick lock my cot and get some food.

At 6.00am Marg is cleaning. I go and play with the doggie. We play lots of things like horse racing. The cat and the dog go against each other.

At 8.00am Homer goes to work and Bart and Lisa go to school. I play with Homer's newspaper. I play pirate ships and that is the sail. Then Marg makes me a paper hat out of it, that's funny.

At 10.00am Bart comes home. He is suspended. We have a snack. Bart goes up to his room, that's my boring brother.

At 12.00am Lisa comes home, time for lunch. Now I can watch some real TV, Lisa puts on the Happy Elves. I know what happens, but it is better than Crusty the Clown.

At 2.00pm almost time for Lisa to come home. I start to play with my bricks. Then I use Bart's toy Godzilla to knock them down.

At 4.00pm Lisa has been home for a while, Lisa plays with me. Bart goes off with Millhouse. They take some tomato ketchup and mustard.

At 6.00pm time for me to go to bed but everyone forgets. Homer comes home, in a minute he will go off to the pub when he gets his wallet, but Bart has nicked it. He uses Marg's purse. That is him gone till around nine.

At 8.00pm I take myself to bed.

Thomas McIntosh (9)
Sacred Heart School

A DAY IN A LIFE OF SARAH MICHELLE GELLAR

I woke up at 9.30am and walked down the stairs still in my PJs. I went to the kitchen table and sat down, my mum was there eating some toast slowly as she read the newspaper. My cereal was honey loops, my favourite. When I got to my friend's house (Tara) I stayed there for dinner and tea. I went home at 7.01pm. Then Alison rang me up to ask if I wanted to go to the Bronze. I said 'Yes,' so we went to the Bronze (I wore a black leather jacket with a white top and blue jeans) and came home at 11.00pm, went to bed and went to sleep after a hard day.

My mum woke me up. I wasn't happy. It was Monday and it was 7.30am. I put my jeans and violet top on. I was at school. I met Alison. I got my books from the library. I rushed to class. I was doing science but I was late (Alison wasn't with me). I got in really late, so Mr Vence told me to see him after school. All the classes went quickly. Soon it was time to go home. Mr Vence told me off about being late, then I went home and got to have tea in bed. I didn't feel well. Then I went to sleep.

Madelaine Brearley (10)
Sacred Heart School

A Day In The Life Of A Snake

My name is funny little Lou
I am a snake from the biggest zoo
I live in a hut that's very nice
It's meal time. I'm having mice.

I can see the keeper's juicy leg
I'm going to break it with a wooden peg
And then I'll eat him in one go
Wait a minute it's beginning to snow.

If I leave my little hut
The door behind me will lock shut
The mice are dropping from the roof
I was chewing them then *poof*

My silly brother came out
'Go away' I loudly shout
I bit him around his fat neck
He's made of metal, very hi-tech

I was still biting his neck
Then off with his head
Now it's nearly time for bed
Electricity round my teeth
I hear a funny noise beneath

I slip out of my very nice cage
'Oh my God what an outrage'
Shouts the zoo keeper
The funny noise getting deeper and deeper

I dug right down really deep
The noise sounding like a sheep
I fell far down into a cave
I saw a devil having a shave

He began to shout and screech
He sounded just like a sheep
A hand reached down and pulled me up
Put me in my cage and locked the cage shut

There was my brother without a head
So I thought he must be dead
Then his head zoomed straight back
He dived at me and my view turned black

Was I dead maybe?

Ryan Scadden (10)
Sacred Heart School

A Day In The Life Of Samantha Mumba

6.00am Wake up time to get out of bed.

6.15am I tidy my bedroom and my designer chooses my clothes.

6.30am Get dressed, get ready for my gig at Manchester in front of about 10,000 people.

7.00am I go to my make-up room, my make-up artist puts my make-up on for me.

7.30am Time to do my hair (which is my favourite, I love my hair). My hair gets permed and put up.

8.00am Time to choose my shoes, that's one of my favourites too.

8.05am I'm setting off to go to Manchester. I'm so excited, it's going to be my first gig. I'm nervous and excited.

9.30am I've arrived at Manchester. Now I'm really nervous. I'm just about to go backstage.

10.00am I'm on stage singing to the crowd. It is amazing.

1.00pm The show's over. It was excellent, absolutely great, the crowd was raging.

1.30pm Way back from Manchester.

1.50pm Dinner at McDonald's. I'm having a happy meal.

2.50pm Afternoon nap for two hours, I'm so tired.

4.50pm Teatime my favourites. Burgers and fries.

5.50pm Taking all my make-up off or in the morning I'll look horrid.

6.20pm Take my hair down for bed.

6.25pm Have some supper watch some TV.

9.00pm Got to bed. I'm really really tired.

Georgina Lewins (10)
Sacred Heart School

A DAY IN THE LIFE OF MY BIG SISTER

7.00am My mum came to wake me up, but I didn't listen. I just stayed in bed for another half an hour. My mum realised I hadn't come downstairs for breakfast, so she came charging up the stairs and shouted at me,

'OK, OK,' I said to her, 'I'm coming.'

7.45am Finally I went down for breakfast, where I saw the rest of my family eating toast, eggs and bacon.

8.00am I went to watch TV, where I had a row with my sister over which channel we wanted on.

8.30am In the end, I gave up and went to school with my friend Lisa. We went on the bus, but it was late so we were late for school and our teacher made us write lines. That took us till about break time.

10.00am Break time. I had some cheese and onion crisps (my favourite).

10.30am Maths lesson, which I didn't enjoy.

11.00am ICT, my favourite subject.

12.00pm Lunch time, I bought myself a salad sandwich.

1.00pm PE, very boring.

1.30pm Geography, even more boring.

2.00pm Break time again. By this time, I had a headache.

2.30pm History, my worst subject.

3.00pm Science test, that was OK, because I got full marks.

3.30pm Home time. Hallelujah.

4.00pm Finally got home, had my tea.

8.00pm I felt sleepy, so I had an early night.

Laura Savage (10)
Sacred Heart School

A Day In The Life Of Bart Simpson

I wake up at eight am
and I have my breakfast, then,
my mum Marge has lots of hair
Lisa cuddles a teddy bear.

Quarter to nine I'm off to school
on my skateboard it makes me cool,
got on the bus and saw Millhouse
he'd brought to school a plastic mouse.

Got to school went into class
threw a ball and broke the glass,
the teacher saw a big woodlouse
so I showed her the plastic mouse.

The teacher climbed upon a chair
and Millhouse said
'What are you doing up there?'
The teacher got a bit cross but after all she is the boss
Nelson punched me in the face and I ran home in disgrace.

When I got home I saw my mum
She told me off and smacked my bum,
Then she sent me back to school
I told my mum this was uncool.

She said she didn't really care
So I made fun of her big blue hair.
When I got back to school we were
Studying night the teacher asked me
Where I'd been so I told her about the fight.
Miss told Nelson not to punch
So he kicked me and stole my lunch.

School's over, it was great, got detention
Must stay late, went home and had my tea
Weekend off
I'm *free!*

Jonathan Crossley (10)
Sacred Heart School

A Day In The Life Of Robbie Williams

I set my alarm for half past five
because I have to go perform live
I went and got dressed
In my very very best
I brushed my hair
With so much care
Then I was ready
My driver came round he was called Eddy
It is now half six
I said 'Let's go'
And in the car was a girl called Jo
I travelled fifty miles
And then I was at where I did my trials
I got to the stage
In so much rage
I said 'Shall I start?'
My very first part
I started singing Supreme
All the people started eating strawberries and cream
Then it was time to start it live
There was a big crowd
And they were really loud
I got hold of my microphone
Then I heard the trombone
I started to sing
And then a mobile started to ring
He turned it off
And then I started to cough
When it was half time
I had some lime
I went back to dance
Then in came Lance
I started to do my best
To hope I passed the test

The crowd started to cheer
And then they all bought me a beer
I went back home to find a letter from Rome
And then I went to bed
With dreams rushing through my head.

Helen Sutcliffe (10)
Sacred Heart School

A Day In The Life Of My Guinea Pig

Every Sunday and Wednesday I have to clean the smelly cage out! The best thing about it is that. I wake up at 8 o'clock. Come home from school, clean the cage out. Oh it smells! Do the food as well and spray it with disinfectant. It takes about five hours to dry, then it's a mess anyway. My mum always has something to complain about.

Sometimes my mum does it, then she's only being kind, but afterwards she's back to her own self. When I do it she always says something like 'What's that on the floor? Pick it up.'
She shouts in front of the guinea pig. It'll be deaf by now, but I don't think it is anyway. I'll be glad when it's lost its voice, then it can't squeak.
'Michaela!'
'Yes Mummy.'
'You know what the mess on this floor is? It is disgraceful. I'm not cleaning it up. I do enough of that at work.'
That's an example for you of my mum. Every morning on ITV I watch children's cartoons. My mum says I should not watch children's cartoons in the morning. Mum says that it stops you getting dressed. So I turned off the TV and went and got dressed.

Michaela Wyatt (9)
Sacred Heart School

A DAY IN THE LIFE OF THE TITANIC

Once I was just a metal board, then I turned into a huge ship. Then they painted on the side of me, Titanic. So I knew that my new name was Titanic.

One day I went on a voyage to New York. I was excited as it was my first voyage on the big wide ocean. It was fantastic in the sea because there were dolphins in front of me. It was getting dark and I was tired and cold, it had been a long journey. It was getting misty and the water was getting colder and colder. I hoped the night watch were staying awake. *Bump! Crash! Scrape!* Ow that hurt. As soon as I got away I realised we had hit an iceberg. Oh no I could feel water in my cargo hold. I went down head first. I started to cry. This isn't how my maiden voyage should be. Wait a minute, I could hear people screaming and the violin players still playing. Oh, oh I was going under, my back end was going up. *Crack!* I split in two. One half of me has gone down. My back bit was going up, people were screaming and crying. Then the back started to sink. Goodbye world.

James Rushworth (10)
Sacred Heart School

A Day In The Life Of A Tree

It is very boring being a tree, watching the traffic pass by. In the winter I get really cold with the falling snow. I'm really sad because all the leaves and flowers are falling off my huge boughs. In the spring however, owls and little fluffy rabbits come to nest inside me. In the summer all the leaves and flowers burst into bloom, so I'm very happy all through summer. The autumn isn't that bad but it is the same as winter. At least in autumn I can hear birds singing away madly. But also in the autumn my flowers and leaves start falling out. As slow as summer came, the year melts away slower than ever. And there I am, stood on my own with no one to talk to, no one to listen to passing by. Even the traffic has stopped zooming by. I feel as though I'm shrinking, all the trees around me have been cut down, people call me the lucky tree but, all I am is a lonely tree. I wish I could have all my friends back but no! Every time a new tree is full grown they cut it down. I'm not a very happy tree. Please help me. I moan about it at night.

Sophie McNeill (10)
Sacred Heart School

A DAY IN THE LIFE OF A BIRD

I woke up in the morning sun, stretched my wings and soared down to the ground, looking for something to eat. I spied a juicy worm and before you could say 'hungry' I had it in my beak and was gobbling it up. It was just how I like it, soft and slimy (and delicious of course). I flew up to the clouds. I love it up here. A cool breeze ruffled my feathers. The clouds were all different shapes and sizes, I saw one that looked like ice cream. I noticed my friend nearby.

'Chirp, chirp!' I called.

'Chirpy chirp,' she replied.

I flew over to her. She had caught a huge worm about the length of five eggs. I wish I had that worm, I wouldn't carry it around with me though. I'd scoff it up before some other big bird comes and takes it, maybe she just wanted to show it off. I kept looking at it while we were flying. I was very hungry again. In the end she let me have a bit. It was better than the worm I had this morning.

The sun was setting, glowing a dark red. I heard my mum calling for me in the distance.

'Chirrrp.'

I flew back to my nest, made myself comfortable, then tucked my head under my wing and slowly drifted off to sleep.

Tanith Horner (10)
Sacred Heart School

A Day In The Life Of Geri Halliwell

7.00am Woke up and it was raining. It was not raining men.

7.30am Decided to get up. Had a shower and went down for breakfast.

8.00am Finished my breakfast and went to the dance studios.

10.00am Finished my dance. Now I am going to sign copies of my single.

1.00pm Lunch. Went to the cafe and had a salad sandwich. It was still raining.

2.00pm Went home and fell asleep. I had a dream that I was at number one for the rest of this year.

4.00pm The phone woke me up. It was my record company. They said I had sold over one million copies of It's Raining Men. We talked for a while.

5.15pm I phoned my mum to tell her the good news about my single. We talked about my next single. I was going to rehearse. Then we made arrangements for tonight.

5.30pm I made myself a cup of coffee, turned on the TV, then I phoned for a Chinese.

7.30pm I felt sick so I phoned up my mum to tell her I won't be going out tonight.

8.00pm I went to bed, still feeling a bit sick.

Emily Riley (10)
Sacred Heart School

A DAY IN THE LIFE OF MY BOYFRIEND

6.30 I wake up and turn on my TV
7.00 get out of bed and get dressed
7.30 I go down for breakfast (Golden Nuggets)
8.00 feed my fish
8.30 Catch the bus
9.00 go into school
9.15 into class
First lesson maths
89+89=178 94+94=188 4+4=8
I get all my sums correct
10.40 Break time
10.55 Back into class
11.00 English
I'm writing a letter to the Abbey
12.00 The infant bell goes off
12.10 the junior bell goes off. Out to play we go.
The whistle is blown and I go in for dinner. I sit next to Dominic and Liam who's a mosher

I finish my lunch and stack my chair and pick up my lunch box and bottle and put them away and go out to play football. We stay out for half an hour, then we come in and it was science tests. Oh no I hate tests. Then at 2.20 we got out to break. Fifteen minutes later we come back in. Then we watch a video and at 3.30 the home time bell goes and we go home. When I get home I get changed and go on my skateboard to Crowood with Liam. At 8.30 I come home. 9.00 I get ready for bed. 9.30 I go to bed. 10.00 I get to sleep.

Sarah Gerrard (10)
Sacred Heart School

A DAY IN THE LIFE OF A DOLPHIN

At 9.00am I wake up snuggled between two rocks in a sandy bed, I decide to go for a swim and wake myself up. I come back and have twelve angel fish for breakfast.

10.00am I go off and play with my mates and chase little fish in and out of the coral reefs, oh no . . . I see a dark shape swimming towards us. It's a shark, a great white shark. We quickly swim to a dark cave and hide until danger has passed.

12.00pm My tummy starts to rumble. It must be lunchtime, so I swim off home and have squid to eat.

1.00 Time to go to school. I spend the afternoon learning maths and English.

4.00pm I swim home for my tea. I have clams and oysters followed by jellyfish and ice cream.

5.00pm My mate comes to call for me and we go out to play. We swim round and round, playing hide and seek in and out of ship wrecks. We swim to the surface and see lots of people. We wave and laugh at the people in the boat and they wave and laugh back. We go tired of this game and swim back down to the bottom. We play tig until my mum calls me in and my mate goes home.

8.00pm I settle down to watch television.

9.00pm Feeling really tired after such a busy day, I brush my teeth and snuggle down in my sandy bed and my mum reads me my favourite book which is 'All Dolphins Go To Heaven'.

I'm very sleepy now so good night diary.

Laura Houlihan (10)
Sacred Heart School

THE DAY IN A LIFE OF A MOTHER

I woke up at seven to take Peter and Penny to school. They brushed
their teeth then came rushing down the stairs, but the door was too thin,
so Peter pushed past Penny and knocked over all of the toys, which I
had just picked up. The minute I put their toast on the table, the two of
them walked to the table and ate their breakfast in silence. I took them
in the car, seeing as the school in Oldbre was a long way from Tring.
After they had gone I went to work and sat down on my chair. I went to
pick the children up from school. They watched TV, then had some
dinner. After that they went to bed and they same happened the next
day. For about a month, then things changed because I forgot my kids
stayed for netball practise.

Alice Miller (10)
Spennithorne CE Primary School

A DAY IN THE LIFE OF AN AUTHOR

I woke up early that morning wishing that I didn't have to take the kids to school. Anyway it was Friday. I don't have to take them tomorrow. Louisa and Gary were calling me saying
'Mum, Dad wake up we have to go to school you know!'
I managed to pull myself out of bed. Lazily I walked over to the wardrobe, pulled the door open and I took my jeans out. The drawer opened easily as I picked up a green T-shirt. Downstairs I ran. The kids were at the dinner table already. Shane was walking downstairs in his night-gown.
'What's for breakfast?' he asked.
'Bacon sandwich,' I answered.
'We always have bacon sandwiches, can't we have something different?' moaned Louisa.
'You can have some cereal then,' I said.

At last I've got rid of the kids and Shane. I made my way upstairs. I went up to the loft, grabbed my pen and paper and wrote some more of my story called *The Curse of the Headmaster.* I wrote for what seemed like forever and a day. All I had really written was a page. This book would take a long time to write. The door slammed downstairs. Shane was back from work. I carried on writing when he came up and gave me a kiss on the cheek.
'I'll be downstairs if you want me,' he said.

It's the end of the day. The kids are in bed. Shane and me are watching TV and my story is nearly finished.

Colette Cowley (11)
Spennithorne CE Primary School

THE KING OF THE SEA

It was the coldest day of December in the year 1967. Deep down at the bottom of the Antarctic lay danger that nobody knew about until now.

In a deep, dark cave a loud noise broke the silence of the sea which terrified the smaller fish. The only thing that could make a noise so terrifying, was the mean machine of the sea, he's the fiercest animal in the sea, it's Spike the great white shark, and his teeth are the size of three foot, sharp bread knives.

Silently and swiftly, as he hunts for his prey, he charges like a torpedo, fast and deadly. There are no second chances with Spike on the prowl. His razor-like teeth slicing through the flesh of anything that gets in its way. Spike's dorsal fin was very unusual. It was very pointed, hence his name.

When Spike's in a fight, no matter what happened, Spike would always come out on top. He's a mean, lean, killing machine, at the top of the food chain you would always find Spike. He can locate his prey from miles away using his superior sonar senses.

Spike's capture lead to the end of the great white shark named Spike.

The legend of Spike will go on for years to come.

Kurtis Walker
Throstle Farm Primary School

THE CASTLE IN THE DESERT

On a hot and blistering night, the dog roamed the streets of an old deserted town.

'I wonder where I might get some food' I said, panting madly. 'I've roamed these streets all week and found no food.'

Soon I walked the dark alleys so far that eventually I reached a vast desert.

'Where am I?'

Dawn was coming fast. You could see the sun rising slowly over the horizon. The desert gleamed and shone as the sun lifted its bright face.

'What is that wriggly thing? It's big and brown.'

A sand snake wriggled across the desert and then disappeared into a lump of sand. I ran as fast as I could to escape the jaws of the vicious snake.

'He had quite a big mouth. What is that up there shaped like a house?'

When he reached the large house, he discovered it was a huge castle. It had bright green ivy creeping up the walls, the windows glistened in the sun like flashlights and the chain on the door had old rust and black and red spots of paint. The splintered door opened, slowly and noisily. Now night was falling.

'I'd better get inside. It looks like a storm is heading this way and I don't want to get caught in it!'

I ran into the castle but then the door slammed shut! I'm trapped!

'I can't get out! I'll be stuck here forever!'

And so he was . . . !

Sarah Blackburn
Throstle Farm Primary School

QUEEN BOBO

Queen Bobo was always lazy and beautiful or at least she thought so. She dressed fantastic and her habit was flicking her long sparkly brown hair back on her shoulders.

'Bang, bang!'

'Oh shut up, I'm coming.'

Creeakkk! The door swung open and there was a tall man, brown short shiny hair with a red nose coloured waist coat. With a crash Queen Bobo fell to the floor. She'd fallen in love, she's not that beautiful she can't fall in love.

'Wake up, wake up!'

'Urrrr what happened? I feel awful.'

'I know because you are.'

'That isn't very nice, do you want to stay for dinner?'

'You don't even know my name.'

'What is your name?'

'My name is Prince Goldeneye,'

'Yeah right,'

'I am not joking.'

Prince Goldeneye and Queen Bobo were beginning to like each other, but like a mystery they started meeting each other, even though Queen Bobo was ugly and Prince Charming was gorgeous.

'Laaa, laaa I've got a boyfriend.'

She was very pleased as she brushed her long shiny hair but she didn't know that he had a wig and he had false teeth. Will she find out? Daadaaaa!

The moral of this story is to never judge a person by their looks, but their personality.

Stephanie Morton
Throstle Farm Primary School

THE FAMOUS FREDDY PING

'Hector, bedtime,'
'Yes Mam.'
Hector jumped into bed and began her sweet dreams. In no time she was outside by the canal.
'Hello, my name's Hector, what's yours, if I may ask?'
'I'm the famous Freddy Ping.'
'What are you drawing?'
'You!'
'How can you have, if I have just arrived.'
'It's all in my imagination you know.'
'Or!'
'Plus I knew you were coming.'
'Do you mean that you can look into the future.'
'Yes I can.'
'What is going to happen in the next five minutes.'
'Well, where are we going next?'
'We're off to the secret underground water shaft.'
'Wippee!'
'Come on then! Don't let anybody hear you.'
'Wow, isn't it cool!'
'I made this years ago to keep all my treasures down here.'
'Can I go in the swimming pool please?'
'Yes you may if you want.'
'Thank you, Freddy.'

Hector went into the other room and went in the swimming pool and Freddy was painting.

Freddy, haven't you got any parents?'
'No, they died when I was eight years old.'
'Sorry for asking.'
'Ha, ha, ha, ha, what's up, Mummy dead!' came a shout from the corner of the room.

A gang of mice with leather jackets on and black cool glasses, then they grabbed Freddy and . . .

'Hector, get up, get ready for school.'
'Yes Mam.'

Hector looked around the corner to see if there was a gang of mice.

Natalie Ferguson
Throstle Farm Primary School

THE LOST CHILD

One hot scalding day while the sun was rising across the deadly sand the pond was all dried up as soon as Toad looked out of his window he was shocked by all his favourite food.

'Yippee I am going out.'

He was really excited. He gulped down his breakfast but something caught his eye.

'Who are you and why are you eating all my food?'

'I am a slug, can't you see. Oh people today.'

'What's that!' gasped Toad.

He looked further inside but he couldn't see anything, so he went back, got a piece of rope and a torch and went back to the hole. He put his torch on and saw a huge bottle. He had to chuck his rope over the top and climbed in. He grabbed onto the paper and chucked it out of the bottle.

It said 'Help, I am in trouble. Please bring help. Penny.' Oh gosh a little girl is in trouble. Will he find Penny. Who knows . . . !

Leanna Jordan
Throstle Farm Primary School

WAR

As the dust slowly settled the sound of silence crept across the battlefield.

The silence was interrupted by a cry for help. This was my mission to get this civilian.

As I marched bending down trying to keep as quiet as I could; I kept my gun ready to fire by my side. In the distance I could see an olive green metal object, an army tank. I ran as fast as my legs could carry me, but keeping low at all times.

As the engine gave a mighty roar a loud echo gave way around the battlefield.

As soon as the echo surrounded the area it was like wild fire, bullets were coming from every direction. As the bullets ricochet around me some made loud noises and some made zinging sounds. I crushed anything which stood in my path, all of a sudden I heard a bomb hitting the tank's tracks.

I knew I only had about five seconds to escape from the tank. I slammed the hatch open, I dived as the explosive backlash hit my feet.

I had no idea where I was, I could only see blood pouring from my head. I stared at my blistered and punctured holes in my leg.

As I crawled through the battle zones, spears flying through the air when people dropped to the ground one by one, battered and bruised, only a couple of metres away from the civilian . . .

'I'm coming, hold on' I shouted, as I grabbed the young child, who was screaming in agony with a severed leg. We limped together towards the horizon, standing close together.

Luke Prentice (11)
Throstle Farm Primary School

A DAY IN THE LIFE OF MYSELF

One unpleasant day, when I was woken by screaming, it was my sisters Becky and Laura. They were shouting and screaming about the television changer, when there was this knock on the door. It was a man. He had brown hair and he was quite tall.

He said 'Do you know where your dad is?'

'Yes, he's upstairs. I will go and get him,' I said
and he said 'OK.'

I went upstairs and into my mum and dad's room.

My dad said 'Why are you in here?'

'There is a man at the door. He said he wants to talk to you. He has brown hair and he is quite tall,' I said.

'I'll be downstairs in a minute,' my dad said.

'OK,' I said.

I ran downstairs to tell him, but he was gone. I went outside, looking for him. His car wasn't there and he wasn't there. I went back inside and my dad was downstairs my dad asked me

'Where is he?'

'I don't know where he went. He just went,' I replied.

Seven hours later . . .

'Dad can I watch TV?' I asked him.

'No, now go to bed.'

'Good night everybody.'

And that was my day as me.

Joanna Mason (11)
West Heslerton CE Primary School

A Day In The Life Of King Richard Third's Commander

It was a normal day at school when *poof* I seemed to go back in time to a castle. In the year 1485 on the morning of the 22nd of August, King Richard Third was half way between Leister and Henry Tudor. It became noon and the king and his army had just left the village of Bosworth. Suddenly the king saw the Tudor flag. The king deployed his army on somewhere called Ambion Hill. Finally he saw Henry Tudor and his army.

Richard said 'Whoever the Stanleys join, wins.'

The battle started with cannons from both sides. Then the Duke of Norfolk, wearing a full suit of armour, charged towards the Duke of Oxford. Luckily for my side the Duke was supported by archers who were shooting arrows at the Duke of Oxford. Finally the regiments met fighting. There was the sound of swords hitting each other, and the sight of blood spurting everywhere. Then I saw it. The Duke of Norfolk was hit by an axe and killed. Then the Duke of Northumberland started to leave. Then I saw him. I saw Henry Tudor. He was with his standard bearer and five bodyguards.

The king shouted 'Charge!'

We all charged. The king almost hit Henry, but his standard got in the way and then it happened. The Stanleys charged at us. I was fighting for my life when the king was killed. I was just about to be hit, when I went back to school.

George Trowsdale
West Heslerton CE Primary School

A DAY IN THE LIFE OF MY HAMSTER

This is Ivy-Buttons. She's a long-haired, very beautiful, golden hamster. I consider her very beautiful because she has three black spots on her back. I call them buttons. Now I'm going to tell you a story Ivy-buttons once had.

It all began with another hamster called Nibbler.
'Mum, is Nibbler going to stay in my room?' Genny said.
'Yes I think so!' said Mum.
Ivy-buttons was thinking what she was going to do at that moment, but when she heard another hamster was going to stay in her bedroom she came back to earth with a big bump. Then the cage came in. To Ivy-buttons it was five floored, ten tunnelled, over-flowing with food, five starred hotel!

Ivy-buttons sulked all day long until night-time when a surprise awaited her.
'Psst!' whispered Nibbler.
'What!' said Ivy-buttons.
'I can get you out of there!' Nibbler said.
'Yeah right!' said Ivy-buttons angrily, 'I've tried ever since I've been here!' Ivy-buttons lied.
'Well you didn't try very hard did you!' laughed Nibbler while chewing the bars of his cage.
To Ivy-buttons' amazement however the door flew open.
'Wow!' she said, 'Can you open mine too?'
'Sure!' said Nibbler walking over to Ivy-buttons' cage.
In two minutes Ivy-buttons' cage was open.
'Thanks,' mumbled Ivy-buttons at Nibbler.
'Don't mention it!' laughed Nibbler. 'Come on, let's go!'
'Umm, I guess so!' muttered Ivy-buttons.

'I know,' shouted Nibbler 'let's play . . .'
Meeeoooowwww!
'Run,' Ivy-buttons shouted, 'Cat!'

And that is how Ivy-buttons' story ends. (And in case you are getting worried, everything was alright!)

Genevieve Lee Edwards (10)
West Heslerton CE Primary School

A DAY IN THE LIFE OF DAVID BECKHAM

One day I went to see a football match with my dad. We went to watch Manchester United Vs Liverpool, it was the big match. We set off after dinner, they were playing at Old Trafford, Manchester's home ground. We went on a bus. It was a long way from my house in Scotland. The match was great, Manchester won 2-0 over Liverpool, so that means Manchester go through to the final to play Manchester City.

When we got home that night I went straight to bed, when I fell asleep I had a dream about being David Beckham. That morning when I woke up I couldn't believe my eyes, I had a frown, I had a bald head and I felt like a proper footballer. Then I realised that I was David Beckham and the final was that night. I was in a different house and there was a girl. It was Beckham's wife, Posh!
'Do you want to go out today before the match?' she said.
'No, I had better not, I should get to the stadium,' replied Beckham.
They got to the stadium and he went to the locker room where all the players were waiting. When the match started I was on the right wing with Giggs on the left wing, we got off to a flying start and scored in less than thirty seconds! I crossed it in for Cole to head it in. It stayed like that for the rest of the match.

Kristian Wilkinson (11)
West Heslerton CE Primary School

A Day In The Life Of James Bond

I got up hearing villains entering the house. So I picked up one of my many grenades and walked downstairs. The first one had a dagger, but I soon kicked him out of the house. I did that to all of them except the last one. This is where the grenade came in handy. I pulled his belt off, put the grenade down his trousers, kicked him out of the house, *bang!* I went upstairs, got my briefcase, kissed the 10,000 wives goodbye and got to work.

When I got to work I said hello to O, no P, no Q! We went to the study. The first new piece of equipment was a P.A.N.T. parachute and nuclear torpedo.
Q said 'You put this over your trousers and click this button on your watch and walla! You have the answer!'

On the way back to my house, Q turned up on my watch.
'Triple O Seven is that you? In twenty-four hours a plane will try to crush you!'
Woosh! A giant aeroplane had nearly hit me!
'Oh yes!' Q said 'I meant twenty-four seconds!'
I grabbed the wing of the plane and I went near the window, smashed the glass and went in! When I got in, I got into a fight but soon won. I then clicked the button and a torpedo blew out of the P.A.N.T! I clicked the button again and a massive parachute came out! I floated down safely.

When I got home I kissed my 10,000 wives good night and went to bed.

Patrick Young
West Heslerton CE Primary School

A DAY IN THE LIFE OF MICHAEL OWEN

One day when I went to do some research on the computer about Michael Owen, I found out that he is a fast football player. And then the screen went black. The next thing I knew was that I was standing in the middle of a pitch. I saw Beckham on the right, then I heard a whistle being blown. The ball was passed to me. I had to think quickly. I passed it to Heskey. He said run through the middle, so I ran as fast as I could. I had the ball crossed through to me. I headed it into the back of the net. The crowd went wild, then I realised that I was Michael Owen. I was against Manchester United, then another whistle went. It was the end of the match. Liverpool won 1-0. After the match Hesky and I went to this bar called The Queen Vic. We met Beckham and Scholes. So we went over to talk to Beckham.

He said 'Why did you knock us out of the champions league?'

'It is just the way it is,' said Michael Owen.

'You're not good enough,' said Hesky.

'Come on then,' said Beckham.

But then I started to feel dizzy. I opened my eyes and I was back home, so I ran downstairs to tell my mum.

I shouted 'Mum I just went through that computer.'

'That's it, I'm taking that computer away.'

James Bailey
West Heslerton CE Primary School

A DAY IN THE LIFE OF MY PONY

I've always wondered what it is like to be my pony. I've always wondered what grass and hay taste like. That night it all began when I wished on a star. I wished that I could be my pony for one day. I am going to tell you a story.

I woke up that morning, I was lying on straw, I looked around, I realised I was in my pony's stable, 'Yuk,' I was covered in poo.

I forgot to say my pony is called Romany, Silver is my sister's pony. Silver neighed to me, he said 'They're coming, it's feeding time.'

A few minutes later I said to myself 'I didn't like the food, but the hay was very nice. I didn't like walking on four legs. I wanted to go home but I remembered I had wished to be my pony for a day. I would just have to wait.

My dad's helper, Andrew, took all of the ponies to the paddock, I could not wait till I got back to my bed with nice food. Just then it started to rain so Andrew put all the ponies in the stables. I waited for hours till the village clock struck 12. I tried to keep my eyes open but I blinked. I was in my bed and that is the end of my story.

Becky Mason (10)
West Heslerton CE Primary School

A Day In The Life Of A Sheep

I was woken by the sound of another sheep bleating, I got up off the green, green, tasty grass and, to my surprise, it was a ewe giving birth. I wondered why Farmer Tibbs or his wife weren't here, they usually came here to the field at the back of their house to watch, and sometimes help.

I will walk over to her and see if she is OK. By the time I get there, she probably will have already given birth.

Five minutes later, I got there. 'Hey Linda (Linda was the name of the ewe giving birth), are you OK?'
'Yes, I'm OK, and so are my two little cute twins.'
'Have you decided on names for them yet?'
'Yes, I have, they are called Daisy and Dilly,' answered Linda.
'Oh, they are very nice names, congratulations, I will have to go now, I need a little drink of water, so bye!'

So I started to walk over to the stream, oh sorry, I haven't introduced myself yet, my name is Bill and I am a two-year-old, well-bred, black ram. I live in fields and I have done since I was a lamb. Unfortunately my mother died when giving birth to my younger sister. Her name is Gill, she is a white sheep with a lovely personality.

Oh, I am here at the stream, this is where all the sheep have a drink, slurp, slurp!

'Wake up, Bill, wake up!' called Diane, Bill's mum, 'it's only a dream.'
'What? What? Oh, I'm not a sheep,' answered Bill (now human).
'No, you aren't a sheep Bill, you're a human!'

Beth Clay
West Heslerton CE Primary School

A Day In The Life Of Eddie Irvine

I got up at 6am. I got all my racing gear, I went down the long narrow stairs in our mansion. When I got downstairs my friend was waiting outside. I let him in and we had a cup of tea. We went outside and I got my Jaguar F1 racer, and put it in the truck, we only lived about five miles away from a famous track called 'Silverstone'.

When we got there, I put my fire mask on and my helmet, then my gloves, while my friend checked the car. When I jumped in my car and had done two laps round the circuit, I saw my friend running towards me. I stopped. I smelt horrible smoke! I got out of the car and the back oil tank was on fire. I grabbed my fire extinguisher and put the fire out. My friend put a new oil tank on.

We went to my house and put the Jaguar away. We had a cup of tea and my friend went home.

The next day we had a big Grand Prix race at Silverstone. I came second, Ralph Schumacher won.

Joe Clay
West Heslerton CE Primary School

A DAY IN THE LIFE OF 'THE THING'

Kirsty and Lorna went for a walk one day. Lorna's mum said 'Don't go to the cave of life.'
'Why Mum?' said Lorna.
'Because the thing lives there.'
'Oh Mum,' said Lorna,
'Yes?'
'What is the thing?' asked Lorna.
'It's a big long snake.'
'Cool. Goodbye Mum.' And they ran off, When Lorna got back home.
'Mum?'
'Yes?'
'Can I go to Kirsty's house to sleep?' asked Lorna.
'Yes, you can go to sleep at Kirsty's.'
Lorna got her things together.
Kirsty lived next door to Lorna. Next day there was a knock at the door and it was Ellie.
'Hi,' said Ellie, and Kirsty said
'Do you want to go to the cave of life?'
'*No,*' shouted Lorna.
'Why Lorna?' asked Ellie.
'Because the thing lives there.'
'Oh no!'
'What?' said Ellie and Lorna.
'Some people have gone to the cave of life.'
Ellie was a scaredy-cat. 'Do we have to go?'
'Yes, we have to go.'
'Oh why?' said Ellie, and they ran off to the cave of life. When they got there the people went in the cave and then came out. Lorna, Ellie and Kirsty went in the cave and killed the snake and they were the queens of China.

Lorna Gledhill (9)
West Heslerton CE Primary School

A DAY IN THE LIFE OF TOBY

Hi, my name's Kim and I have a dog called Toby who's a black Labrador. Anyway, I'll begin my story.

It all began on a warm summer's evening when I was calling Toby to come inside and have his tea.
'Toby, Toby,' I called. I heard him howl. I thought I'd better go and have a look. So I went outside and found him lying in a hole at the back of the garden. It was a very deep hole, but it didn't look deep. So I climbed in and fell to the bottom. Then all of a sudden the wind flew back into my face. I didn't know what was happening. My mind went a complete blur and I flew into Toby. My Dad came outside and called my name. I was meant to be sleeping at my friend's so he thought I had already gone.

My dad fetched me and Toby inside to have Toby's tea. It tasted disgusting. I didn't know how Tony could eat it. His fur was hot and itchy, it felt as if I had measles. At 10.00 at night, Toby and I went into his basket, it was cold and hard.

Soon it was morning so Toby and I went outside. All we did was walk, walk, walk around the garden. Soon we went to the shop with my mum and then came back. We were tired and I wanted to change back to myself. I don't know who, what or why I had gone into Toby. Somehow, but I don't know how, I just appeared next to Toby, picking flowers.

This was a strange experience, and I hope that nothing like what happened to me, happened to you.

See ya!

Eleanor Mennell (10)
West Heslerton CE Primary School

A Day In The Life Of A Rugby Player

One day, Ben was going to Twickenham to open a match between Malton and Cross-Gate. He had to get the bus from Malton Rugby Club at 5.30am and the bus left at 6am. On the way, Joe, Ben, Callum, Bob, Sam, Patch, Ted and Tom all had Game Boy except Bill. He had a portable TV, 8cm in length and 5cm in width so we all watched Bill's TV while the mums and dads played on the Game Boys.

After three hours we stopped and had some food at McDonald's then set off again. After an hour we arrived there but to our amusement it looked like a pig sty outside but inside it looked like a rugby pitch. On the pitch we went in and out of the cones, then we had to tackle. Ben missed Bob. Then Malton came out of the tunnel onto the pitch so we went off the pitch and got changed and went back out and watched the match. Malton won the Tetleys vase for Malton.

On the way back after three hours, we stopped for tea and then we got on the bus and went back home.

Thomas Milner
West Heslerton CE Primary School

A DAY IN THE LIFE OF ELLIE, LORNA AND KIRSTY

One day Lorna was going for a walk with her friends, Kirsty and Ellie. They were 24 miles away from home and it was very cold. Ellie saved the day, she heard and felt a very warm fire so they went to get warm. Lorna and Kirsty were tired so they all went to sleep. Ellie was getting warm next to the fire. Suddenly she saw a snake on Lorna. Ellie was a heroine. She saved a baby girl off the road.

When they woke up in the morning, they set off home.

'I am weak,' said Kirsty, 'can we rest for a bit?'

'No, we have to get back so stop moaning, cry baby.'

'I'm not a cry baby.'

'Yes, you are,' said Ellie, and Lorna laughed.

'You will get this spider down your top,' said Kirsty.

'Sorry.'

'Thank you,' said Kirsty, 'now come on.' 'Be quiet I can see hunters, quick bob down,' said Kirsty, 'they are catching pheasants.'

'Look, a van, we can pinch it,' said Ellie.

'You are rubbish at driving.'

'No, I am not. If we crash don't be scared.'

'Yes! We are home, can we go to your grandma's?' said Ellie.

'Yes,' said Kirsty. 'Hi Grandma, can we come in?'

'Yes.'

'This house is good,' said Ellie.

'Oh no,' said Lorna, 'a cat is in the road.'

Ellie jumped out of the chair and stopped the car from knocking the cat over. She picked it up and brought it home and she gave it some food to eat. Ellie went outside to say sorry to Lorna and Kirsty.

'We are sorry too,' and we never went far away again.

Kirsty Whitley
West Heslerton CE Primary School

A Day In The Life Of A Horse

One day there was a girl called Liz, she was ten years old with a pony called Silver.

Liz was digging in her back garden when suddenly a bottle flew up into the air and landed in front of her. She took the lid off and a ghost flew out. It said 'I'm here to grant you a wish.'
Liz shouted *'Cool!'*
She didn't know what she wanted the wish to be.
Liz's mum shouted 'Tea is ready.'
'What are we having for tea?' asked Liz.
Liz's mum said 'We are having meat, mashed potato, carrots, swede and sweetcorn.'
'Thanks Mum.'
They had finished tea and Liz had gone outside to do Silver, she had the bottle with her. Liz took the lid off and the ghost few out. It said 'Have you decided yet?'
Liz said 'Yes, I want to be Silver.'
'OK *Flash! Bang! Thump!* She was in Silver's body; Liz said to herself 'It is weird walking on four legs.'

 She didn't know where she was at first then she was at a show and she had someone on her back. Liz was standing next to the ring, inside the ring there were fences. Liz went into the ring next, she got a clear round and came 2nd and won a big rosette.

Liz woke up in the morning and didn't remember a thing.

Laura Mason (10)
West Heslerton CE Primary School

A Day In The Life Of My Pet

One day my rabbit had run away, I looked everywhere for it. When I went upstairs I found my rabbit on my bed but it had died.

My mum took me to the pet shop and I bought a goldfish and a dog. We went home. Dad had gone somewhere in his car, but we didn't know where.

I phoned Nicky to see if he wanted to come and play with my dog and I. 'Okay,' said Nicky. We went outside and played with the dog, the goldfish was swimming around in his bowl. Nicky threw the ball and it went into the other garden. The dog just sat there. I said 'Good boy.'
Tracey said 'Hello.' She is my sister. Tracey took my goldfish off me so I told Mum, she said it was hers in the first place. I went to Nicky's house and we played Lego. At teatime we had an argument about the goldfish.

Annabel Watson
West Heslerton CE Primary School

A DAY IN THE LIFE OF SPOT THE CAT

I woke up from a lazy night sleeping on my chair. It was raining, I knew that I was going to be bored! I was so hungry, I went to my bowl, 'Oh it is empty, miaow, and miaow, that might remind them to come and feed me,' I said to myself. 1 hour 40 minutes later they came with my food. 'Yes! It is salmon!' I was really happy, it was my favourite food. When I had finished I went back to sleep, but not long after, I woke again.

'I think I will explore the house, it is very big. I wonder where I should go. Upstairs? Downstairs? In the kitchen? I know, I will go to the cellar to see if there are any mice?'

On the way I saw a dog.
'Woof, woof,' went the dog.
'Miaow, miaow!' I was scared. I ran and hid away, the dog went past me, I was relieved. I continued on my way to the cellar. There was one mouse. I pounced on it and killed it. Someone had closed the door. I was shut in the cellar. 'Miaow, miaow.'

The dog heard me and barked, then someone came and let me out. I went back to my chair and fell straight to sleep.

Anne Lumley
West Heslerton CE Primary School

A DAY IN THE LIFE OF AN ANT

It was another sunny day in the small North Yorkshire village of Scagglethorpe, the birds were singing as David Thornton trudged down the road for another boring day at school. As he walked along, he saw to his surprise, an ant's nest.

'I wish I was an ant,' he sighed. 'No school, no nagging parents, just a free easy life . . . what, what's happening to meeee . . .?' David hit the floor hard. 'Where am I' he said as he stared at the alien landscape around him.

Something silver caught his eye, he walked over to it, and it was reflecting something big and red.
'Aahhh!' he screamed as he spun round . . . and saw, to his surprise, nothing. Then it struck him, he had turned into an ant.
'Hey you!' shouted someone.
'Y ye yes?' David stammered, too afraid to turn round.
'Get back to work, slacker, before you go to the Queen,' he replied.

He went down into the mine, and what a terrible sight met his eyes! There were ants that looked the same age as him, carrying large, heavy rocks.
'Get down below,' growled an ant, 'we need to move all those rocks by tonight.'

After three hours of work and a severe beating David wanted his old life back.

Suddenly, there was a loud ringing in his ears. He stretched out his aching arm . . . and turned off his alarm clock.
'Hooray!' he shouted, jumping out of bed.

'What's happened in here?' his mum asked, 'it looks like an ant's nest.'

Sam Ward (10)
West Heslerton CE Primary School

A Day In The Life Of A Dog

'Sandy, here girl, c'mon!'

'W-w-what? Oh, now I remember, woof, woof.'

'Good girl, out you go.'

'Hi, I'm Sandy - a three-year-old golden retriever - and that's Lauren (my owner). Today will probably be the usual boring same. Normally the most exciting things in my day are:

Dinner time, walkies and *bedtime.*

You would probably think being a dog would be real fun (yeah, right!). Here's me going on about my boring average day. I'm not going to go on anymore, I'm just going to give you a timetable:

7.30am   Lauren wakes me up.

7.35am   Lauren lets me out into the field (I head for the oak tree for a good sniff).

8.25am   Lauren lets me back in.

8.30am   Lauren goes to school, her mum leaves for work, (her dad left ages ago).

8.35am   After I've checked the coast is clear, I slip through the hole in the fence; head for the butcher's (he always gives me a bone).

8.45am   I finish my bone and run to the park to get some exercise.

9.00am   I get back home for a nap.

3.25pm   Lauren gets back from school then takes me for *walkies!*

4.00pm   We finish our walk (if it's not raining).

7.35pm   *Dinner time!*

7.45pm *Bedtime!*

Seems pretty boring - well, it's alright at weekends because Lauren plays with me - if you ever wished you could be a dog, my advice is don't wish it again. ´

Sarah Jaques (11)
West Heslerton CE Primary School

A Day In The Life Of A Bird

'Hi, my name is Saffron, I am a little goldfinch and I live at the bottom of a huge garden. My nest is in the middle of a hedge. In the summer it is full of blackberries but at the moment there are just spiky branches, which are good for keeping the cats out, but not if you're trying to get out!

There are lots of other birds living in the hedgerow with me, so I'm hardly ever lonely. Anyway, enough of the talking because the sun is rising, and when the sun rises so do the birds.'

'Come on, feeding time everyone!'

'Oh, that's one of the young swallows. You see every morning, when the sun rises all the birds gather at the big oak tree to feed. So, I'd better get going.

Look, there it is, the big oak tree. Come on, let's eat! Most birds eat bugs and grubs, but sometimes the humans leave bird food out for us.

Ah, that was nice! Now I'll gather some big feathers for the nest. Here we are, a nice big leaf, I'll use it for the nest. I must be going now because I've got a lot of things to do, bye then, see you tomorrow.'

Helen Carrie (10)
West Heslerton CE Primary School

A Day In The Life Of Percy

Percy is my cat, he sleeps on the sofa and sleeps there for about an hour. Then he goes out to do his business and he sharpens his claws on the tree. Then he climbs the tree. For his breakfast he has cat biscuits and for his tea he has cat meat. He sleeps with Henry and Pooh but not Winnie because nobody likes Winnie because Percy keeps fighting with her.

Every time we have some food, like fish and chips, he always begs for some but we don't give him any unless there is some left and we then we give it to him and the cats. Percy is 11 years old in December. He is older than me. Henry is 5, Pooh is 2 and Winnie is about 9. When they do their business in the grass we have to pick it up with a plastic bag and put it in the outside bin.

Percy has brought a mouse in before, alive, just to show off and he eats it while we are there.

When Percy sleeps on us he snores very loudly. He purrs and slobbers on us. When he is asleep he can still smell food like chicken. So he comes up to us and asks 'Can I have some?' He smells the food next door because they have barbecues so he goes over and gets fed chicken.

Hannah Cooper (10)
Withinfields Primary School

A Day In The Life Of My Puppy

One day I woke up, had a little scratch and a drink. Then I saw out of the corner of my eye, my owner approaching me and my cage. So I sat down with my sad puppy eyes and then I greeted my owner. My owner said 'Do you need to go to the toilet?' So I trotted outside to do my business. Then I saw a bird fly past.

'Max!'

It was dinner time.

'Bark, bark,' I shrieked. Dinner time is my favourite meal. I ran like the wind to my house. After dinner I had a little nap then I woke up and played with my mum. My tail had an itch so I bit it.

'Almost bedtime Max,' my owner called so she put me in my cage and I went to sleep.

Rebecca Bull (10)
Withinfields Primary School

A DAY IN THE LIFE OF MY BROTHER

It's ten o'clock, I groaned, time to get up. I got out of bed and got dressed, then I walked into the kitchen and got some breakfast. I had milk and some toast. I had to go into University at eleven. It was half-ten, ten minutes to get there so I had twenty minutes to listen to some music, which I did. After twenty minutes I set off. I walked along the grass carrying my work.

My lesson today was going to be about cartography. In our lecture we had to do a lot of listening so it was a bit boring. After the lesson some of my mates and I went to play football on the grassy land outside our Halls of Residence. We just kicked the ball around, but didn't have a proper match. After a while we went in and got some dinner, just a sandwich though. After dinner some of us set off to our lessons. This lesson was maths. My lesson was very long.

By the time I got home, I was very, very hungry. I decided to go to Headington and to get something from McDonald's. I got a Big Mac and a super-size fries. I ate it there and made my way home. At home I did some of my work and then listened to music while I had my supper. After that I went to bed.

Emma Rothery (10)
Withinfields Primary School

A DAY IN THE LIFE OF MY MUM

My mum gets up at 7.00 in the morning. and gets dressed and makes herself a cup of coffee. Then she goes and gets the baby eagle owls and opens up the shed to let the goose and the bantams out and throws them some corn to eat. She then comes back in and drinks a coffee. Then she hangs the washing out.

She then goes upstairs and wakes everyone and has a wash, brushes her teeth and puts her make-up on for work. She then gets Ely dressed and washed. Mum then wake us up, again collects all the washing and comes downstairs with Ely. She puts the washing in the washing machine then gets Ely's breakfast. My brother and I come down for breakfast and my mum tells us to go and feed the animals. We watch a bit of TV then go to school. My mum goes to work then when she comes home she washes up and hangs the washing out. Then she feeds the owls (all owls) and puts our tea on. Dad comes home and we have tea all together.

My brother and I wash and dry the dishes while my mum does our lunch and gets Ely ready for bed and then she goes and feeds the baby eagle owls, and puts the animals in and shuts the shed. She brings in the washing and folds it up and puts it on the stairs to take it up and put is away.

My mum then does a bit of paperwork for my dad and puts Ely to bed and relaxes for the night.

Zoey Doodson (10)
Withinfields Primary School

A Day In The Life Of Paige

'Hi Dadda,' I said. My dadda lifted me out of the wooden cot and took me into the bathroom. Shortly after, I was wrapped up in a towel and carried into my parents' bedroom and laid on the bed. My mummy dressed me and took me downstairs to watch 'Tweenies'. She sat me in my chair and cooked my porridge.

I heard two voices coming downstairs and into the living room, Fern and Niall, my older sister and brother. After my porridge I brushed my teeth and played on my see-saw outside. I went on the grass to play, but oh, I fell and was black with mud! Mum saw me and carried me inside and cleaned me up.

Dadda came downstairs and I heard him say to Mummy, 'I'm late for work, it's 8.15am, see you later, bye kids.'
I said 'Bye Dadda.'
Today I am going to 'Bananas in Pyjamas', with my mummy, Fern and Niall. Later my mummy said, 'Paige, it's 10.30am, time for a nap, so upstairs to bed.'

I woke up later and shouted, 'Mummy!'
She came in the bedroom and carried me downstairs for dinner. She put my coat on and fastened me in the car. I couldn't wait to go to the show. We set off and arrived very soon and met Jessica and Georgina, my family's friends. We found our seats and watched the show. Later my mummy cooked tea, chicken nuggets and smiley faces, my favourite.

After watching Tweenies, my dad came home, but I had fallen asleep.

Natalie Smith (10)
Woodfield CP School

A Day In The Life Of Kirsty Owen

Once again Monday came around, the first day after half-term. My name is Kirsty Owen. I'm a normal ten-year-old schoolgirl and every day starts the same, slowly and reluctantly I get up, but today I actually wanted to, for the last couple of weeks I've been bored not learning anything and not seeing any friends.

Dressing rapidly and checking my bag, I was ready to go, but my brother's friend hadn't arrived yet. As soon as I spoke, there he was dawdling down the road. My mother shunted us off to school.

The first lesson was maths, my favourite. Shortly after came English which went on forever. But the best part was five minutes away . . . lunch! It wasn't an exciting lunch, just some sandwiches, crisps and the odd biscuit but I'd rather have that than a Sunday lunch when I'm playing a netball match.

Quickly the netball players were on the way to the match. The first game was with some hard opponents, that's when everything went wrong. I fell over and sprained my foot, there was no way of playing now.

Later that day, we were on the way home, by that time it was past 8pm, so I decided not to have any tea. Shortly after I brushed my teeth sleepily and I limped to bed.

This is a normal day for Kirsty.

Kirsty Owen (10)
Woodfield CP School

A DAY IN THE LIFE OF WHISPA THE DOG

I awoke to thumping of feet in 148 Walmersley Road. Up out of bed into the untidy kitchen, ready to chew people's socks and play with the humans.

'Whispa! Come here.' That was a human voice, Alex. Before I went to greet her I slurped some water down my throat and trotted into the hall. My favourite human, Alex, took me outside.

As I waddled back inside I could smell my puppy chicken and rice food. Yes. There it was, waiting for me. I gulped it down. I loved my food especially the new sort they had started to give me.

Just then, another bunch of thumping feet came racing down the stairs and the two humans, Beth, a little human, and Mum. She told me off for biting her feet, but I suppose that's what mums do. I played with Beth, it's nice to, because she lets me bite her feet. Later on it was time for my nap so Beth and I lay in my bed and soon fell asleep.

At 12.57pm I woke up and had my yummy new puppy food again and chewed my chew and the stairs for a while, as Beth was still asleep.

I had another little sleep. Life can be so exciting! Alex came home and took me for a walk on the stray, we met a black Great Dane puppy. It was a brilliant game! I was taken home and given my last food, then I curled up and soon fell to sleep.

Allie Lenton (10)
Woodfield CP School

A Day In The Life Of My Mum

Crash, rattle. Letters tumble through the letterbox, waking me. The alarm hasn't gone off. I open one eye but see very little. My bedroom is dark and my bed is too cosy to get out of. 7.14am, one minute before the clock shrieks. I better go down and collect the post. Three bills for my husband, Dave. One letter addressed to me - Helen Birch. Opening the three letters has to wait until the snoring has stopped. I will wake the girls.

On the taps go, all isn't normal. Thick golden syrup oozes from the taps, Without realising I put my hands under the tap. I scream loudly. My husband comes and so do Lauren and Joanna. They manage to drag mc from this mess.

Later, everyone is ready. Because it's sunny, I put my thick jumper and trousers on and fly to work on the vacuum.

There seems a lot of post. The telephone doesn't seem to have stopped - everyone wants to know when their furniture will arrive - ggrrr!

10 o'clock, I'm ready for my coffee. I need to milk the cow - then it's ready. I check for e-mails and pay some bills. 12 o'clock - I'm really hungry. The girls should enjoy their zebra sandwiches!

I travel home for some tiger sandwiches. Back to work, more coffee and phone calls. I travel back home at 5 o'clock. After a tea of grasshoppers, I put the girls to bed, watch television and I then go to bed.

Joanna Birch (9)
Woodfield CP School

A Day In The Life Of My Mum

One night at my friend Mel's house, we were upstairs telling spooky stories in her room. Her room looked really spooky and dark whilst the orange wallpaper reflected onto the bed.

At 7.30 in the morning, her dad woke me up by shaking us really hard. I woke up lazily and sleepily, I knew it was school today so I swiftly swung my feet over the edge of the bed and dressed myself.

Mel's dad isn't as bad as he sounds but my dad is. For instance, if you are cheeky he will wash your mouth with soap and water if you are naughty he will bang your heads together. So there's my dad for you.

Later on, when we were meant to be going to school, we hid under the bed until Dad found us and banged our heads together. Then we were given lunch. During lunch we copied my dad by swinging our slippers on our big toes until they flew off.

After lunch we were sent back to school and then I had to say goodbye to Mel and go home with my dad. For my punishment I had to do the washing up after tea. Tea was horrible because Dad made me eat it cold. Yuck! Then I accidentally dropped all the plates in the sink and they smashed, so I was sent to bed.

That day was the worst day of my life.

Abigail Taylor (10)
Woodfield CP School

A DAY IN THE LIFE OF TONY BLAIR

All was calm and peaceful at Downing Street. It was Thursday, 7th June and it was a breezy spring day and the pink blossom was coming off the trees. It was the day of the election. The birds were singing joyfully.

Leo was screaming. Cherie woke up. I looked at the clock, it was half-past six, time to make breakfast and look forward to the election results.

After breakfast, I looked at my letters I had received. It was now time to look through the morning newspapers to check the opinion polls.
The phone rang, I picked it up.
'We have to go to a meeting in five minutes,' I said panicking.
I dressed quickly. I was holding Leo. We were already late. Leo was making noises and was sick all over my new suit.
'We're going to be late,' I said crossly.
We arrived at the meeting. To my astonishment everyone had gone.
I looked at my watch, it was 8am.
'The election count starts at 9am,' I said.
As the time came nearer, I gradually became more nervous and more butterflies came into my stomach. The time had come. I read my speech and everybody clapped.

They had counted the votes.

'Tony Blair is re-elected MP for Sedgefield,' the returning officer said.
I was so proud of myself.
I made another speech; I was overjoyed.

Zara Sekhavati (10)
Woodfield CP School